W. H. Seartoss

458 SPECIES IN FULL COLOR

SEASHORES

A GUIDE TO ANIMALS AND PLANTS ALONG THE BEACHES

by

HERBERT S. ZIM, Ph.D.

and

LESTER INGLE, Ph.D.

Professor of Zoology, University of Illinois

ILLUSTRATED BY DOROTHEA AND SY BARLOWE

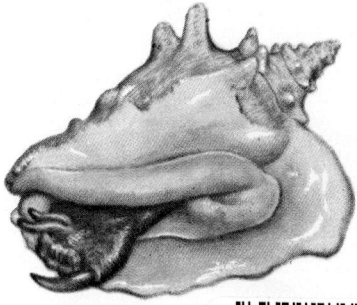

W9-BKB-379

A GOLDEN NATURE GUIDE

GOLDEN PRESS • NEW YORK

FOREWORD

Where land and ocean meet at the shore, a mysterious world begins. Here the drama of the sea and its life comes to a focus. This book—a seashore primer—will help you understand and enjoy this unique zone.

Many persons helped to make our book possible. First to be thanked are the artists, Sy and Dorothea Barlowe, for their excellent work. Valued suggestions and criticisms came from R. Tucker Abbott, E. J. Alexander, Frederick M. Bayer, William D. Clarke, John E. Fitch, Ira N. Gabrielson, Howard R. Hill, Alexander C. Martin, Harold A. Rehder, Paul C. Silva, and Alexander Sprunt IV. Donald F. Hoffmeister, Natalie and Milton Zim, Frank C. McKeever, Rosalie Weikert, Donald P. Rogers, and S. A. Farin helped with source material. The New York Botanical Garden, American Museum of Natural History, Smithsonian Institution, Philadelphia Academy of Natural Sciences, Los Angeles County Museum, and University of Illinois Natural History Museum also gave generous assistance.

H.S.Z.
L.I.

Copyright 1955 by Golden Press, Inc. All Rights Reserved, Including the Right of Reproduction in Whole or in Part in Any Form. Designed and Produced by Artists and Writers Press, Inc. Printed in the U.S.A. by Western Printing and Lithographing Company. Published by Golden Press, Inc., New York 22, N. Y.

Library of Congress Catalog Card Number: 61-8318

HOW TO USE THIS BOOK

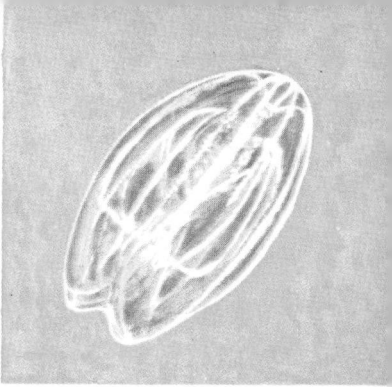

Rainbow Jelly—a Comb Jelly

The United States has about 88,600 miles of tidal shoreline, and nearly every mile is a place of potential interest. Everything on the shore is worth your attention, from the magnificent sweep of the sea and sky to the forms of life that dwell on the beach or are cast up there. Hunting for shells has long been a favorite pastime. This book will help in identification, but it is more than a guide to shells. It attempts, in a simple way, to give a picture of life at the shore, from soaring gulls to worms and clams.

You can use this book best if you begin before you go to the shore. Read these introductory pages. Thumb through the book to get acquainted with marine plant and animal life. Remember that shells and seaweeds cast up on the beach may look quite different from the living plants and animals. Remember also that, yard for yard, some shore areas are much richer in plant and animal life than any other areas. Don't expect to identify everything you find. Use the key on the next two pages as a starter. With its help, you can place most things within a major group. Then look further to see if your specimen or one like it is illustrated. Illustrations show only the most common of thousands of species. Yours may be similar to, but not identical with, the one illustrated. Sizes given are average; allow for variation. For more detailed identification use scientific names (pp. 154-157), the books listed on p. 154, and museum study collections.

PLANTS

ALGAE—non-flowering plants, of varied form—seaweeds. PAGES **18-35**

Blue-green Algae (1,500 species)—thread-like or branched filaments; some slimy. **20**

Green Algae (5,000 species)—some sheet-like; most are branched or unbranched threads. **21-24**

Brown Algae (1,000 species)—mainly large, cold-water plants; often with air bladders and "leaves." **25-30**

Red Algae (2,500 species)—smaller, more delicate than brown; live in deeper, warmer water. **31-35**

FLOWERING PLANTS—a great group (250,000 species), with roots, stems, leaves, flowers. Only common dune and shore species are included. **141-146**

ANIMALS

SPONGES (3,000 species)—simple, many-celled animals with numerous pores; varying form and color. **41-43**

CORALS and KIN (5,000 species)—soft, cup-like, with tentacles, stinging cells. Some have limy skeletons. **44-52**

COMB JELLIES—jellyfish-like; no stinging cells; some with paired tentacles. **53**

WORMS—four to twelve groups (phyla), with distinct characteristics; some round, some flat, some segmented. **54-57**

TO SEASHORE LIFE

MOSS ANIMALS and LAMP SHELLS—a small, diverse, and ancient group with two main divisions. **58-59**

STARFISH and KIN (6,000 species)—with radial bodies (five divisions). **60-66**

ARTHROPODS—jointed-legged, with external skeleton; a vast group. **67-79**

Crustacea (25,000 species)—jointed legs and segmented abdomens; include barnacles, crabs, lobsters, shrimp. **68-79**

MOLLUSKS or SHELLFISH (80,000 species)—soft-bodied, shelled. **80-140**

Chitons — primitive mollusks with 8-plated shell. **81**

Bivalves (Pelecypods)—animals with shell in two lateral halves. **82-110**

Univalves (Gastropods) — animals with single coiled shell, or no visible shell. **111-137**

Squid, Octopus, and Kin — well-developed head and tentacles; usually no external shell. **138-139**

Tusk Shells—a small group with tusk-like shells. **140**

BIRDS—of the 70,000 species of vertebrates, including sharks and fish, whales, and other marine mammals, only shore birds are covered in this book. **147-153**

OBSERVATION is the key to science and to enjoying shore life. Watch carefully; details of form and movement cannot be seen otherwise. Observe at the beach. Take live specimens home for study. Make a salt-water aquarium and keep small specimens alive. The practice of keeping notes and records will make your observations sharper, your understanding broader.

CLOTHING is important in your ventures—warm clothing and rubber boots in colder months, a bathing suit or the equivalent at other times. Wear sneakers to protect feet. Goggles and snorkel will give experienced swimmers entrée into a new world. Beginners be careful!

EQUIPMENT can be simple. Use binoculars for birds, a pail and other wide-mouthed containers for algae and small animals. A trowel, a spading fork, and a kitchen or putty knife are handy. Later you may find landing and dredging nets a help; with them, collecting from a small boat is rewarding fun. A good magnifying glass or, better still, a low-power microscope will give you a chance to study small invertebrates while they sport in a few tablespoons of sea water. For preserving sea animals, use rubbing alcohol, slightly diluted. Mollusks can be cleaned by boiling. Starfish and kin can be dried in the sun.

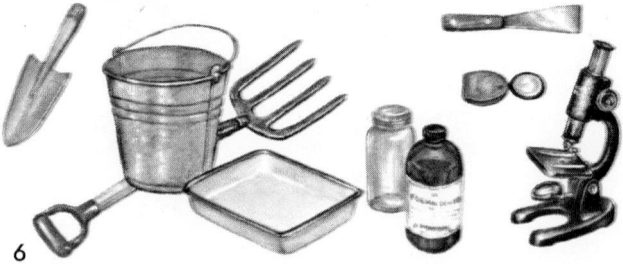

LOOK all around you. Try different types of shores, as plants and animals vary greatly on mud flats and rocky and sandy beaches. Look under rocks. Dig into sand and mud. Wade out, especially at low tide, to find specimens you may miss otherwise. Don't overlook the algae and shells washed ashore after storms. Some smaller creatures are the most attractive.

GET HELP in identifying your specimens. Besides this book, try the more advanced ones listed on p. 154. Experts at museums and universities are often glad to help. Most marine biological research stations welcome visitors. The U.S. Fish and Wildlife Service, Washington 25, D.C., has technical publications on marine species of economic value. Dealers in shells may help you in identification and can supply specimens for your collection.

CONSERVATION of the rich resources of our shores is your responsibility. Everyone who enjoys the wind and tide, the terns, and the shells underfoot has a stake in preserving our shores in their natural state. Pollution of shore waters by ships, cities, and factories is a serious problem. Animals are harmed by chemical wastes or lowered oxygen content of water. Support groups working to protect our seashores and their natural resources.

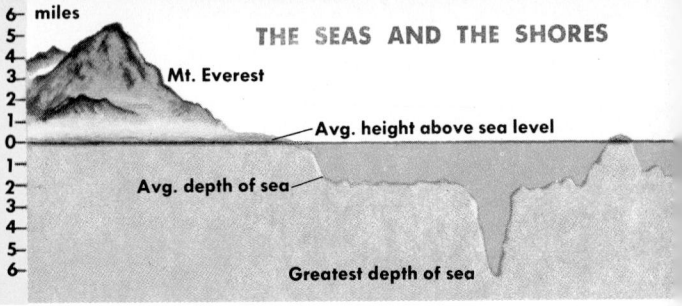

THE SEAS cover about 72% of the earth's surface—61% of the northern and 81% of the southern hemisphere. The average height of all the land is about ½ mile. If the surface of the earth were smooth, an ocean 2 miles deep would cover it. The weight of the seas in tons is estimated at the figure 12 followed by 17 zeros. This water, a great reservoir of heat, profoundly affects climate. In it oxygen, carbon dioxide, and other gases are dissolved; so are many solids, which make up about 3½% of the weight of the seas. These solids include more gold than has ever been mined and enough iron to last man thousands of years. The United States alone has 88,600 miles of coastline; the world, probably over a million. Shores are rich in plant and animal life, and here important geologic changes are taking place.

Seas cover nearly ¾ of the earth's surface.

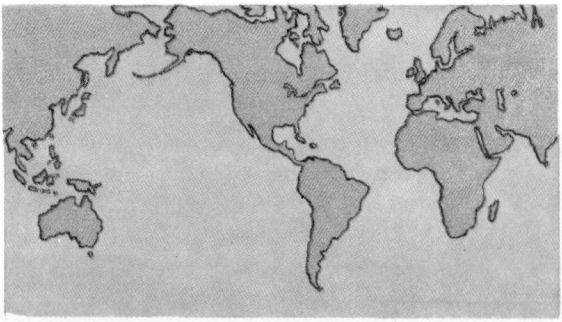

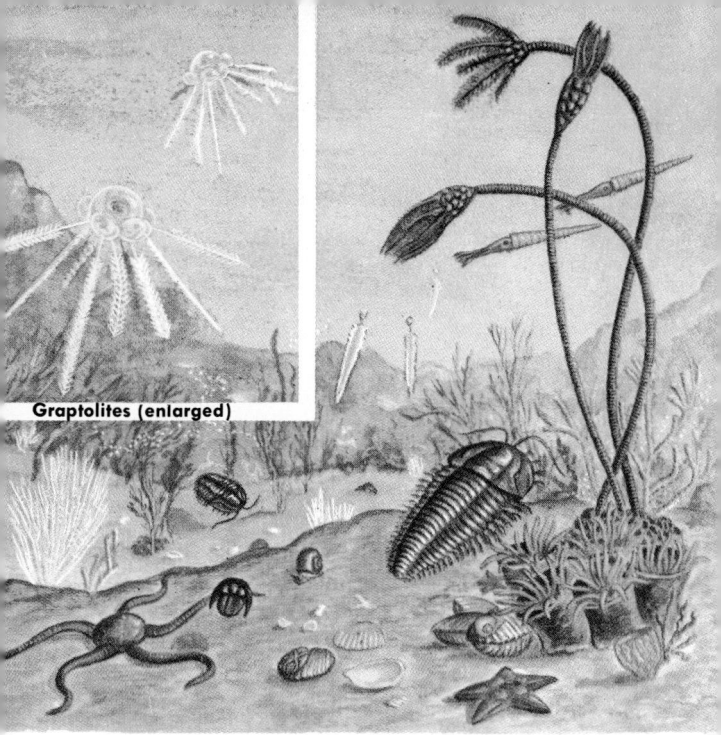

Graptolites (enlarged)

Shallow-water life about 400 million years ago

LIFE went on in the seas for millions of years before plants and animals ventured on to land. The transition was a slow one, and in it the shore zone was a critical area. Some ancient sea animals have survived and have changed so little they closely resemble their fossil ancestors; others changed greatly. But land animals still show traces of their origins. The liquid portion of your blood, and that of other land animals, contains in solution many of the same chemicals as sea water.

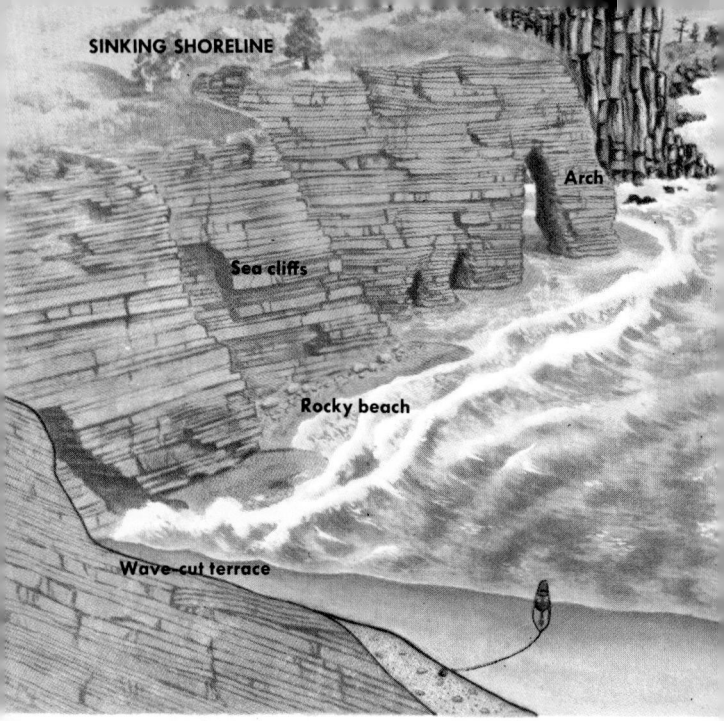

SEASHORES, the battleline between land and sea, are of two main types. Where shorelines are sinking, the sea carves the land into sea cliffs, terraces, arches, caves, and rocky beaches. These dramatic shores and headlands may encompass shallow bays where sand and pebbles form protected beaches. A wealth of plant and animal life is often found on rocks between the tidemarks. Tide pools are unique places to study shore life—both plant and animal.

Large areas of sloping sea bottom are often exposed

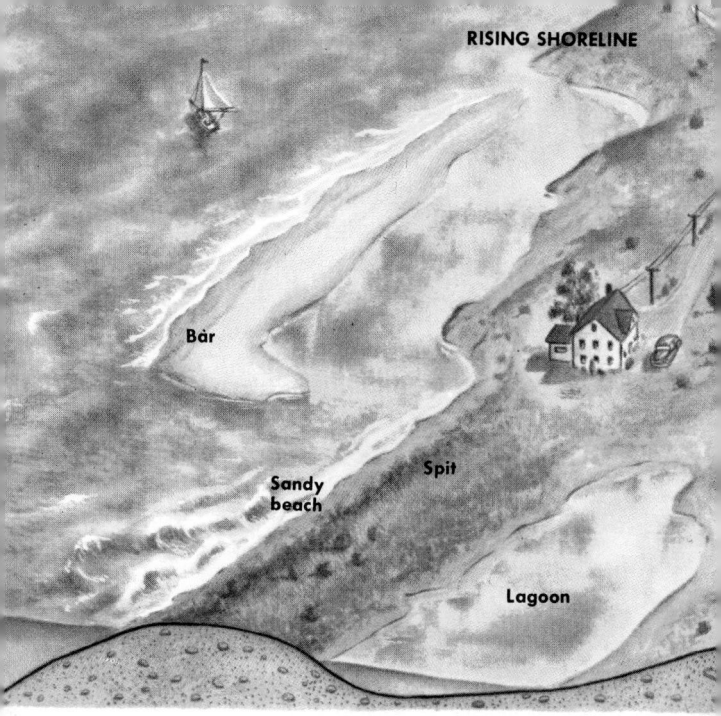

along rising shorelines where land is uplifted. Sand, moved by waves and currents, builds up an offshore bar or barrier beach between a protected lagoon and the breakers. Bars and spits also develop. Wind moves dry sand into shifting dunes. Brackish tidal marshes may form with abundant plants, birds, and smaller animals. Life along sandy beaches is often distinct from life on rocky ones. Different kinds of shellfish, worms, and crustacea live on each. Some sandy beaches may be quite barren, except for things washed up.

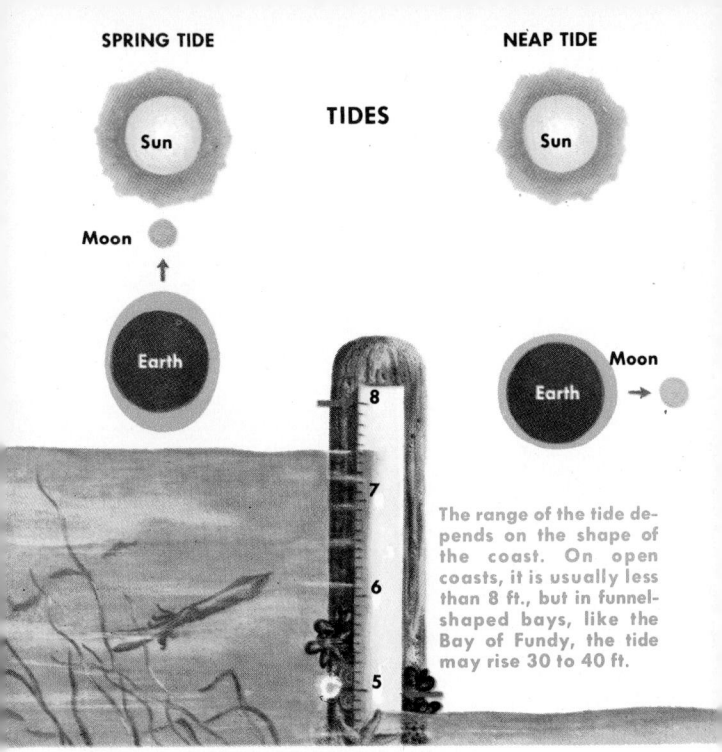

TIDES result from the gravitational pull of moon and sun. The moon, much nearer the earth, has a stronger pull than the sun. When sun and moon are in line with earth and pull together, high tide is highest, low tide lowest. When they pull at a right angle, tides are less extreme. As the moon revolves and the earth turns, the tidal bulge moves around the earth. Tides on the Atlantic and Pacific coasts come about an hour later each day. Shapes of the ocean basin and of the coasts affect tides. The Gulf of Mexico has 1- or 2-ft. tides; elsewhere they are 4 to 8 ft. or more.

WAVES are caused by the winds. The steady push of wind gives the water its rolling, rising and falling motion. As the water moves up and down, the wave itself moves forward. Waves have little effect a hundred feet down, but as they move into shallow water near the shore, the friction of the bottom causes them to rise higher until they tip forward in an arc and break. The breaker, like a miniature waterfall, rushes up the beach till its energy is exhausted. Currents and undertows along the shores may be set up by wave action.

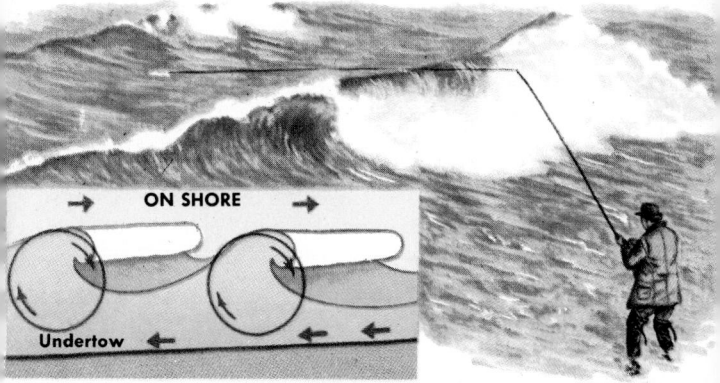

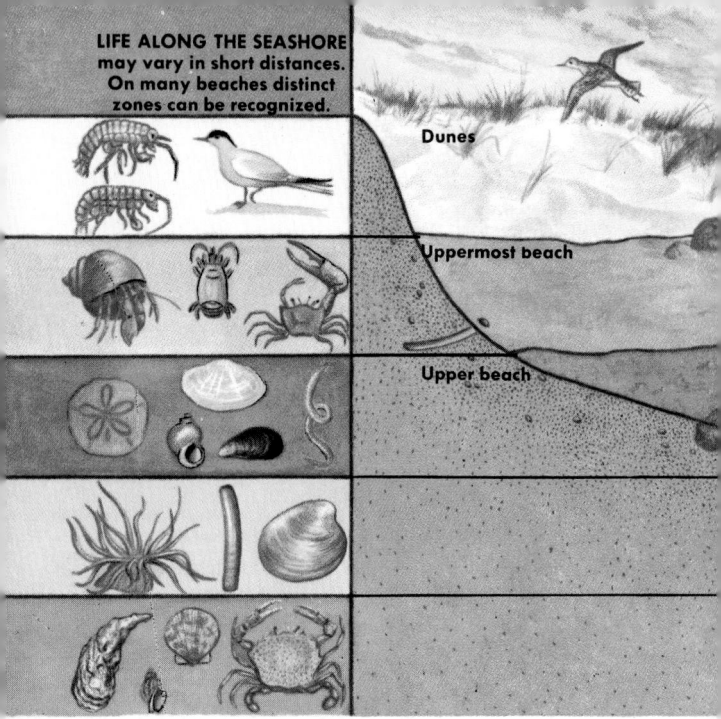

SHORE LIFE differs on rocky and sandy beaches, and on exposed and protected ones. Each bit of beach shows how plants and animals live together in certain broad life zones. First and highest is the dry beach or dune area. The uppermost beach is reached only by the highest tides, storm waves, and ocean spray. The upper beach gets wet by tides twice daily, but the plants and animals are more adapted to land and air than to water. In the middle beach, which is covered with water most of the time, plants and animals are normally less exposed to air and are

more harmed by drying. The lower beach is almost always submerged except during the very lowest tides and so is exposed no more than twice monthly—during the "spring" tides.

Plant and animal life form characteristic communities within these broad zones. Each is adapted to a particular marine environment and its food supply. Water temperature due to latitude or offshore currents, salinity as affected by streams, and pollution from ships and cities modify the shore life of a region.

Foraminifera Diatoms (top) Copepods

PLANKTON is to the sea what grass is to the land—the basic food. All forms of plankton are very small, often microscopic. Billions upon billions live in the sea. Most common are the diatoms, plants of colder waters which furnish almost nine-tenths of the food in the ocean. Diatoms and other microscopic plants are more common than dinoflagellates and the plankton animals. Among the latter are included single-celled animals, small jellyfish, and copepods—tiny relatives of lobsters and crabs. Plank-

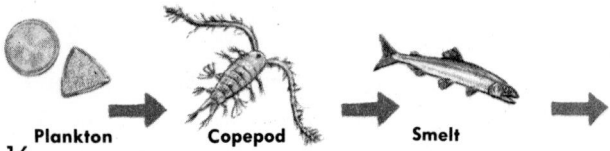

Dinoflagellates Radiolarians

ton serves as food for small fish and other sea animals which, in turn, are eaten by larger species. One authority figures about 10,000 lb. of diatoms are eaten to make 1,000 lb. of copepods, and 1,000 lb. of copepods produce 100 lb. of smelts. The 100 lb. of smelts, when eaten, give 10 lb. of mackerel which, as food, make 1 lb. of tuna. Caught, canned, and eaten, 1 lb. of tuna increases man's body weight by only 0.1 lb. Such food chains illustrate the interdependence of sea life.

MARINE ALGAE

Seaweeds, or marine algae, are easy to collect, preserve, and study. Of about 18,000 kinds of algae, some live on land, more in fresh water, but most are marine. These grow attached to rocks, piles, and even boats. Storms wash up deep-water species. Any rocky beach or wharf is good collecting ground. Take a pail, spoon, knife, and putty knife along. Wear appropriate clothing. Scrape algae free and drop them into your pail of sea water. Later, at home, float one plant at a time in a large tray or dishpan. As it floats, arrange, trim, and spread it. Slip a sheet of heavy white paper under it. Raise slowly, letting plant settle and water drain off. Most smaller specimens will adhere and dry in place. Larger seaweeds can be photographed, or preserved in alcohol or 6% formaldehyde. More interesting than preserving specimens is detailed study of them when alive. For this, a high-powered microscope and high-powered patience are needed.

2. Float specimen into position. Raise paper and remove slowly.
1. Float specimen in pan of sea water. Slide heavy paper beneath.
3. Cover with cheese-cloth. Dry between blotters, mount, and label.

BLUE-GREEN ALGAE are a widespread group of some 1,500 inconspicuous species, both marine and fresh-water. They form dark scums on mud, rocks, and piles, or appear as a velvety fuzz on boat bottoms. Most are dark bluish-green in color and can thrive in polluted waters unsuited for other algae and animal life. Some species live in hot springs; others give the Red Sea its color. Identification is difficult without microscopic examination of the thread-like, often gelatinous plants. Mermaid's Hair lives on mud, rocks, and piling in shallow water of both coasts. The simple, unbranched filaments are curled and matted.

GREEN ALGAE, including over 5,000 species, are more common in fresh water and on moist soil than in the sea. Marine species are found along all shores but are more abundant in warmer waters. These are smaller and more delicate than the great kelps, and prefer more shallow water. Some green algae are single cells. Better-known marine species grow as filaments, irregular sheets, or branching fronds. Some tropical species take lime from sea water and help build "coral" reefs. No algae have roots, stems, or leaves like higher plants. Blue-green algae have no specialized sex cells; reproduction is vegetative, cells splitting off to form new plants. In the green algae, sex cells are formed, though vegetative reproduction also is common in nearly all species.

Codium, a very common and widely distributed marine green alga, occurs along the southern Atlantic, Gulf, and Pacific coasts. Sometimes called Sponge Seaweed because of its soft, sponge-like texture, Codium has many branching stalks. It is closely related to Bryopsis (p. 23).

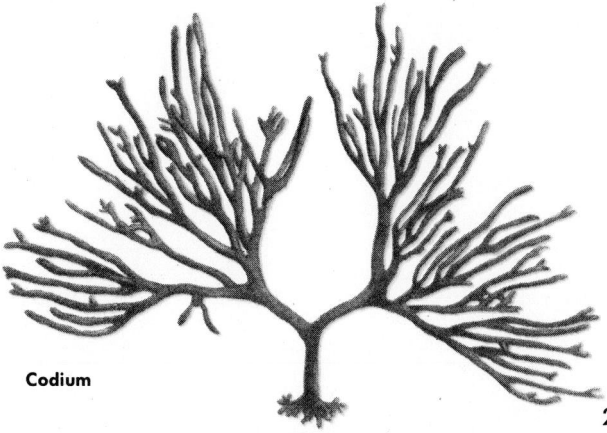

Codium

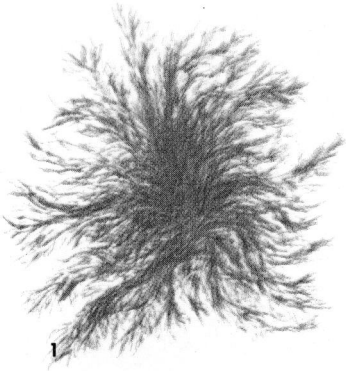

1

CLADOPHORA is a group of variable species, quite common on the north Atlantic Coast. Plants vary from silky, compact, green tufts to coarser filaments 3 to 12 in. long.

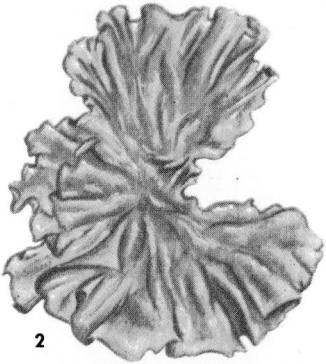

2

SEA LETTUCE is common on both coasts. Largest of the green algae, up to 3 ft. long, it is sheet- or ribbon-like. A number of species, typical of shallow water, grow on rocks or in mudflats.

3a

ENTEROMORPHA, 4 in. to 2 ft. long, often called "grass," is a common green alga of piers and boat bottoms. Some species are stringy or ribbon-like, others flattened, thickened, or with inflated branches.

3b

1. Caulerpa

CAULERPA is common on sandy and muddy bottoms in warm water and on coral reefs. It spreads by horizontal stems, covering large areas. Fronds, 2 to 4 in. long, are eaten by sea turtles. Plants are variable, some with simple fronds, some branched.

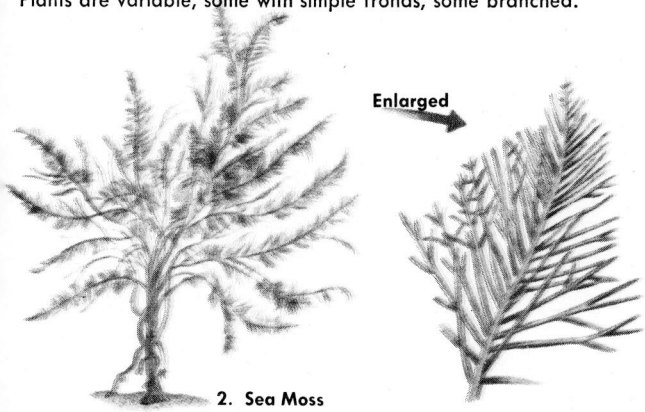

2. Sea Moss

SEA MOSS or BRYOPSIS includes some 20 species which branch and rebranch, giving the plant a delicate, feathery appearance. Sea moss is abundant along the entire Atlantic and Pacific coasts, growing on rocks and piers, occasionally in mud. Plants are 2 to 8 in. long and are a darker green than other green algae. Species are marked by differences in branching and fineness of the filaments.

1. Halimeda

2. Mermaid's Cup

3. Merman's Shaving Brush

TROPICAL GREEN ALGAE are more common than cold-water species. Along the warmer parts of the Atlantic and Gulf coasts are several species, small in size and unusual in form. Oddest is Merman's Shaving Brush (Penicillus), 2 to 5 in. long, shaped true to its name. Several species of Halimeda all have unusual thin, roundish, branching segments with cactus-like growth. Mermaid's Cup (Acetabularia), 1 to 3 in. tall, is like a small, greenish-white mushroom. Patches of these three algae carpet shallow areas.

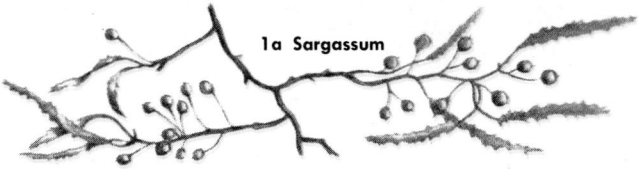

1a Sargassum

BROWN ALGAE include, in the 1,000 or so kinds known, some of the largest and most interesting algae. Brown algae are diverse in form and structure; some have involved life histories. They reproduce vegetatively and by the union of male and female cells, which swim out into the water. All brown algae contain a greenish-brown pigment which absorbs light like the green pigment of green algae. This pigment is effective at medium depths, so brown algae may grow as much as 75 ft. down. Tremendous beds of brown algae stretch along temperate and cooler shores. These algae are used for fertilizer and as a source of iodine and potash. The chemical algin, made from them, is used to make puddings smoother, to finish paper, to apply dyes and inks, and in medicine.

Sargassum, most famous of the brown algae, floats over mile after mile in the "Sargasso Sea" of the Atlantic. Over 150 species, usually 3 ft. or more long, occur widely in warmer waters, but some are found well to the north on our Atlantic and Pacific coasts. Fronds outwardly resemble stems and leaves; air bladders of varying size are common.

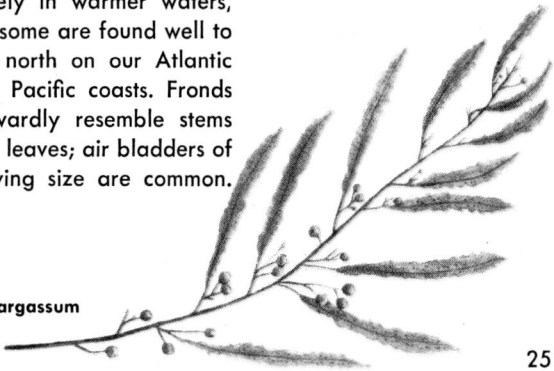

1b Sargassum

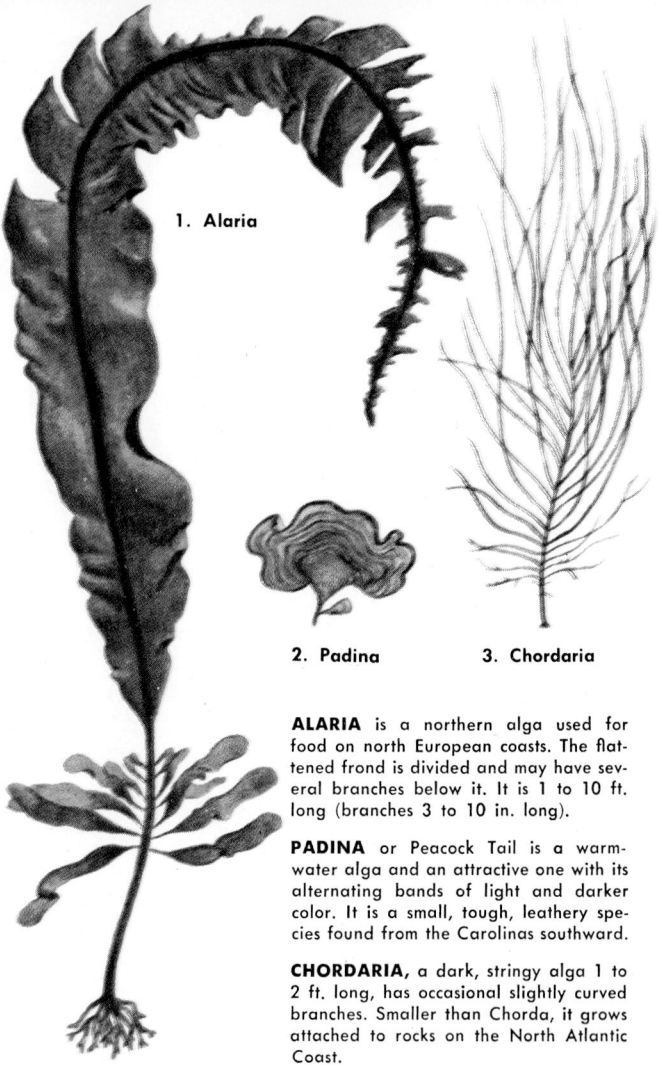

ALARIA is a northern alga used for food on north European coasts. The flattened frond is divided and may have several branches below it. It is 1 to 10 ft. long (branches 3 to 10 in. long).

PADINA or Peacock Tail is a warm-water alga and an attractive one with its alternating bands of light and darker color. It is a small, tough, leathery species found from the Carolinas southward.

CHORDARIA, a dark, stringy alga 1 to 2 ft. long, has occasional slightly curved branches. Smaller than Chorda, it grows attached to rocks on the North Atlantic Coast.

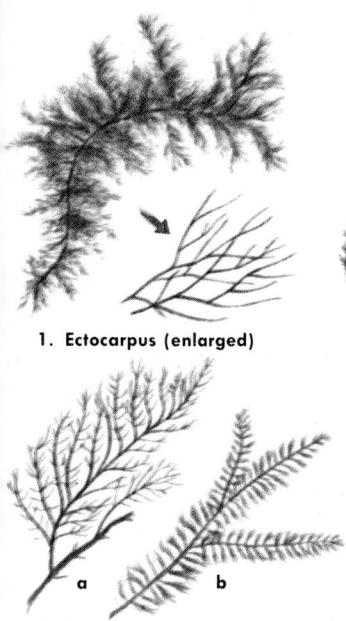

1. Ectocarpus (enlarged)

2. Desmarestia

3. Chorda

ECTOCARPUS includes many species difficult to distinguish. Most have fine filaments in loose or dense tufts. Some are feathery or spongy. Ectocarpus grows 6 to 12 in. long on rocks, wharves, or larger algae.

DESMARESTIA also includes varied species. The most common has thin cylindrical fronds with stiff hairy or spiny branches. A Pacific Coast species has flattened, branched fronds 2 to 6 ft. long.

CHORDA grows as slender, whip-like fronds 3 to 12 ft. long, some bare, some hairy. Common in northern waters, they grow singly from a disc-shaped holdfast. Plants grow anew each spring.

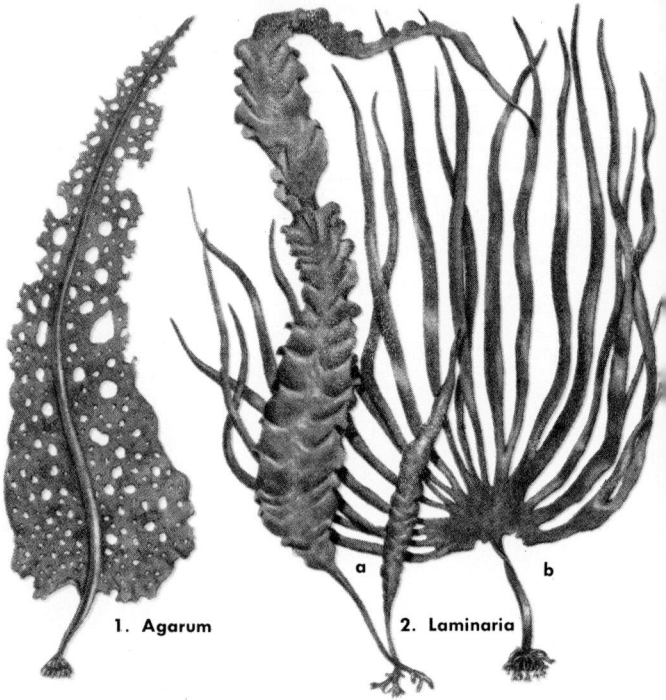

KELPS, the great brown algae of northern waters, are harvested on the Pacific Coast, and thousands of tons are used yearly in chemical industries. In Asian waters, these algae are "farmed" for food. East Coast kelps include Alaria (p. 26), Laminaria, and Agarum. West Coast kelps are larger and more imposing; some grow to lengths of over 100 ft. A tough holdfast anchors the kelps to the rocky bottom; air bladders float the plant to the surface. Kelps grow from the low-tide mark to depths of 100 ft. or more. Nereocystis and Macrocystis include the largest and best-known Pacific species. Sea Palm (Postelsia) is one of the most unusual of all marine algae.

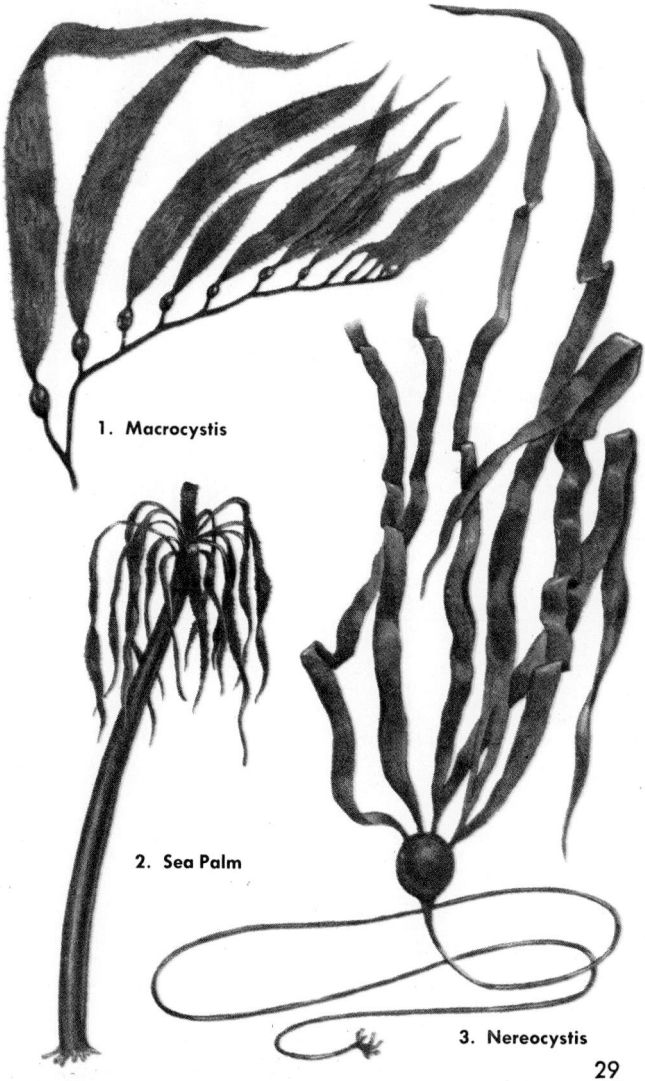
1. Macrocystis
2. Sea Palm
3. Nereocystis

FUCUS (or Rockweed), one of the most widely distributed seaweeds, abounds on all cool, rocky shores. A number of species are similar in structure and habit. All have swollen air bladders along the mid-rib. The well-known life history of Fucus is an example of how seaweeds grow and reproduce. Parts of Fucus, torn loose by waves, continue to grow and may become established as new plants; otherwise, they reproduce by specialized cells. Other brown algae have similar life histories.

RED ALGAE are admirable for delicate color and form. Most of the 2,500 kinds prefer cooler, deeper waters than other algae. Their red pigment absorbs more blue and violet light, which penetrates deepest in the ocean, so red algae can manufacture food at depths of 100 to 200 ft. Species living closer to shore are important in tide-pool plant life. Some lack the typical delicate branching pattern and are coarse, flattened, or club-like.

Several species when boiled yield agar-agar, valuable in medicine and bacteriology. In the Orient, British Isles, and Scandinavia, other red algae—Irish moss, dulse, laver, slack—are widely used as food or for chemicals. Field identification of most red algae is difficult.

Dasya is found from Florida to Cape Cod. The delicate orange-brown to red-purple fronds, with many thin, hairy branches, are 6 in. to 3 ft. long. Look on shells and rocks in quiet, protected areas below the low-tide mark. When taken from the water, the fragile, delicate fronds collapse into a red or purple jelly-like mass. Dasya is a large and well-known genus. A number of species are found also on rocks along the Pacific Coast.

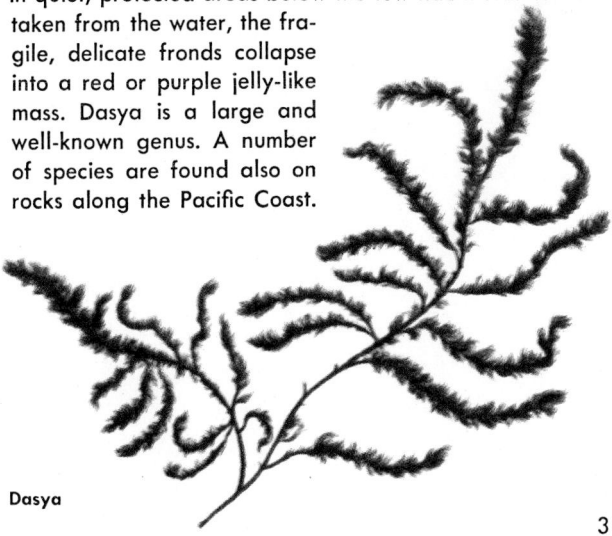

Dasya

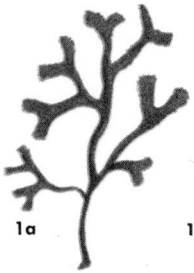

1a

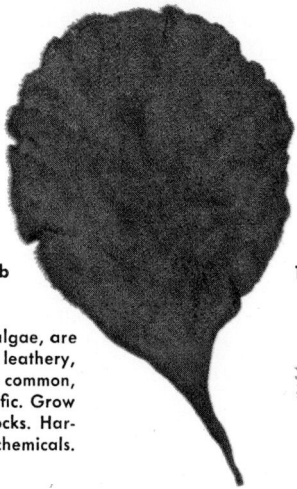

1b

1c

GIGARTINA, odd red algae, are often thick, stringy, leathery, rough, and spiny. More common, more diversified, on Pacific. Grow 6 in. to 3 ft. long on rocks. Harvested commercially for chemicals.

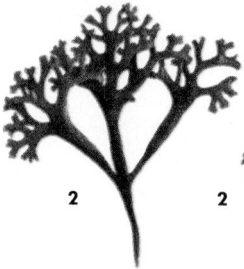

2

2

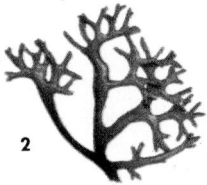

2

IRISH MOSS or Chondrus is found as dense purple or purple-green masses in tide pools and shallows along cooler, rocky shores. Gathered for food and as a source of industrial chemicals.

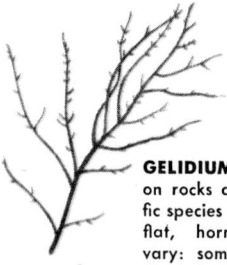

3a

GELIDIUM grows 3 to 6 in. long on rocks along N. Atlantic. Pacific species grow much larger, with flat, horny branches. Species vary: some stringy, some finely divided. Identification difficult.

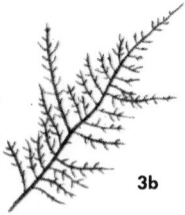

3b

1a

1b

1c

POLYSIPHONIA is a complex group of many species not completely identifiable without a microscope. Finely branched, less than 1 ft. long. On rocks and other algae; Atlantic and Pacific.

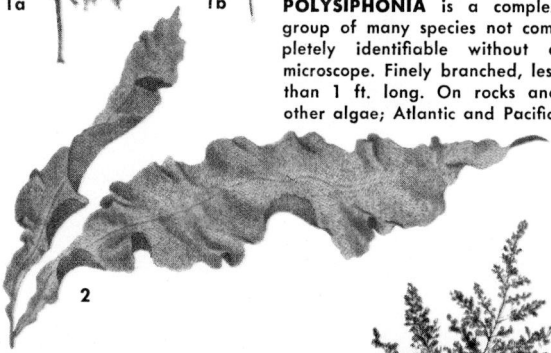

2

GRINNELLIA is a delicate Atlantic species common in spring and summer, on rocks, piles, and shells. Wavy fronds 4 to 12 in. long. Similar forms on Pacific, some with conspicuous midveins.

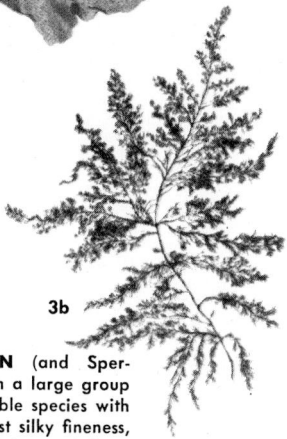

3b

3a

CALLITHAMNION (and Spermothamnion) form a large group of delicate, variable species with filaments of almost silky fineness, 1 to 6 in. long, pink to red. From Florida northward.

1a

CERAMIUM is also a group of small red algae (2 to 6 in.). Use a hand lens to see the tips of the filaments, curved like minute claws. Found on other algae and debris, especially on the Atlantic.

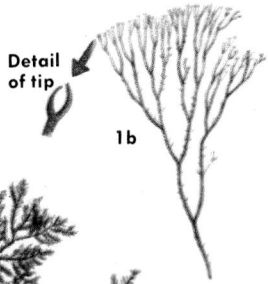

1b

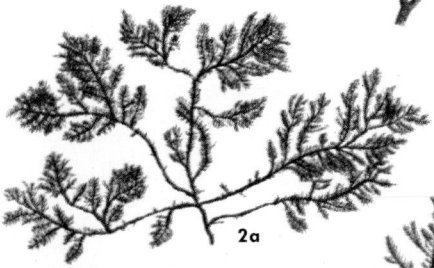

2a

PLUMARIA (Ptilota) or Feather-weed is common on North Atlantic and all along Pacific shores. The dense, fern-like tufts give the plant its name. Prefers deeper water but is often washed ashore.

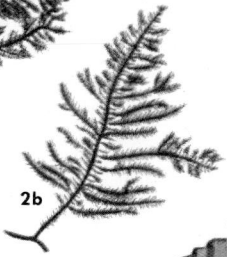

2b

3a

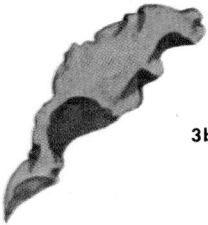

3b

LAVER or Porphyra is often gathered as a food plant and makes an excellent soup. It sometimes looks like a thin, delicate red Sea Lettuce (p. 22), but species are variable in form and color.

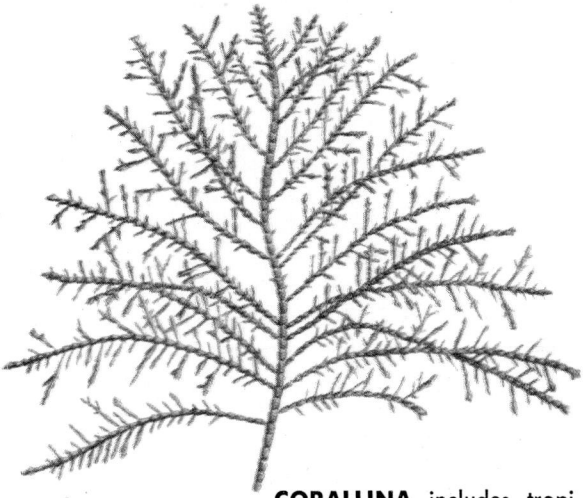

Detail of frond

CORALLINA includes tropical species and those which extend far north into Canadian waters. The plant is hard and covered with a crust of lime. When it is washed up on beaches, the sun bleaches it completely white. The branching of Corallina is always opposite. The segments of the plant are flattened and wedge-shaped. Other coralline algae are found along the Pacific. The ability to deposit lime from sea water is also shared by green algae (p. 24). Such action aids materially in the building up of "coral" reefs.

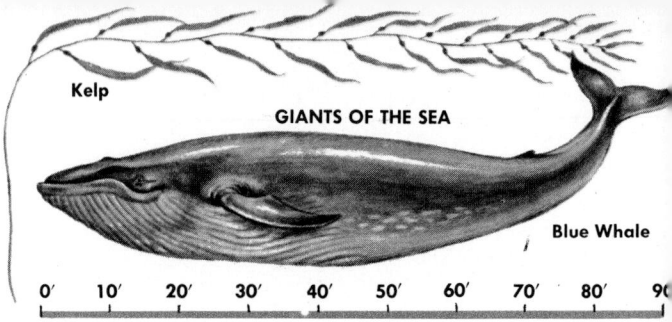

ANIMAL LIFE AND PLANT LIFE in the sea are not distributed at random. They follow patterns as complex, in their own way, as human societies. One factor is the tremendous range in size of ocean organisms. Plants range from bacteria 1/25,000 in. long to giant kelps (p. 28) that grow to over 100 ft. The range in length in the marine animals is about the same, but the much greater range in weight is hard to imagine. Marine protozoa weigh as little as 1/6,000,000,000,000 oz. The great blue whale weighs up to 150 tons—or 21,800,000,000,000,000,000 times as much.

Large and small, these plants and animals are bound together by their water environment, and even more tightly into living communities within the seas. Such communities of plant and animal life are very evident along the shore. Anyone who begins to study shore life will find obvious signs of them. The intensive study of such communities may yield more knowledge and greater satisfaction than the accumulation of many boxes full of shells.

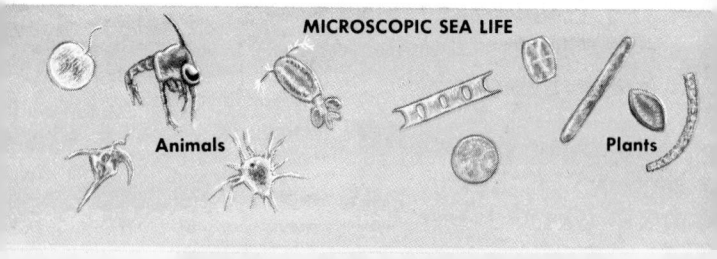

Pacific Coast tide pool

SEASHORE COMMUNITIES are determined by such things as the nature of the shore—rocky, sandy, or muddy. The depth of water or the range in tides is another factor; so are currents, the temperature of the water, and dilution from fresh-water streams. These factors, working together, enable certain plants and animals to survive and develop into communities. Watch for them. Food is supplied by the plant life. Larger animals feed on smaller ones and on plants. Some sea animals can exist in a wide range of surroundings and are found along most shores. Others are selective and exist only when conditions are exactly favorable. These conditions make the difference between a Pacific Coast protected tide pool and the clam-rich mud flats of Long Island Sound.

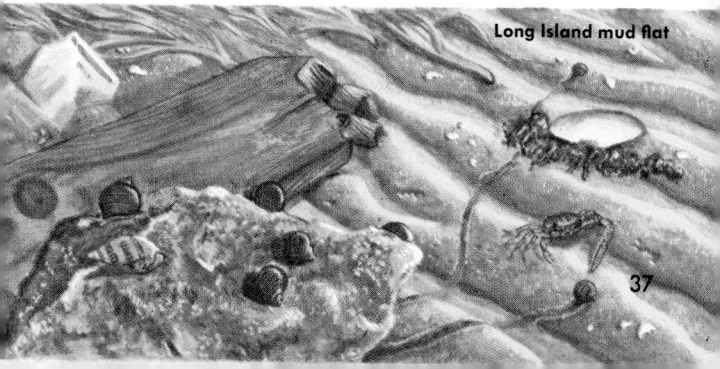

Long Island mud flat

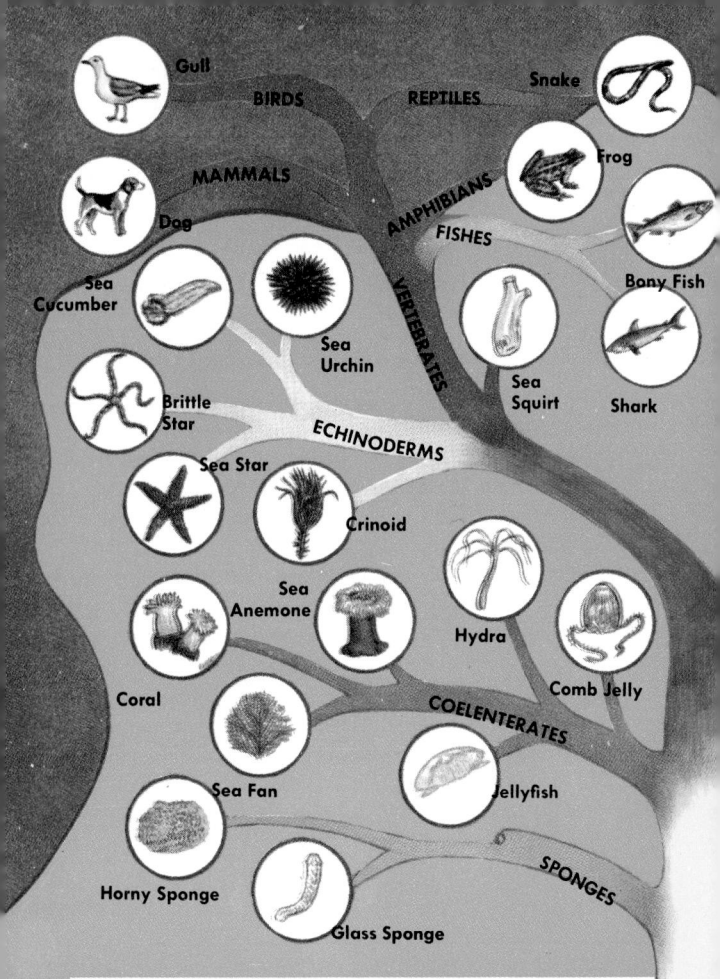

ANIMALS OF THE SEA and of the land are one. Nearly every major group of animals includes kinds that are adapted to sea life. All the animals in each group are

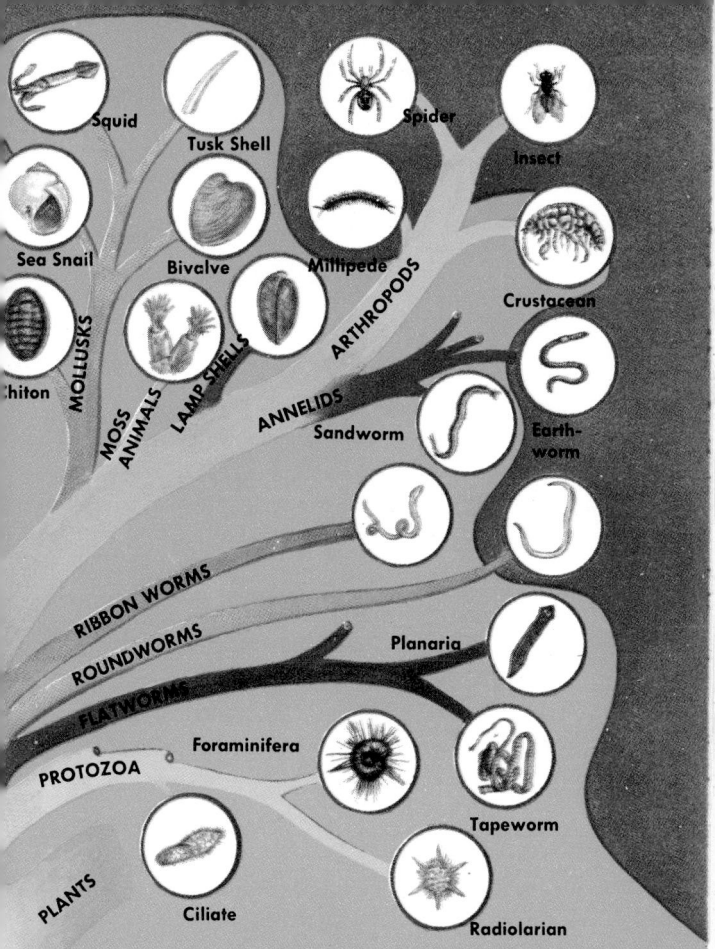

related to one another and have developed from common ancestors. The "family tree" of animal life shown above is a general picture of their relationship.

SEA SQUIRTS (Ascidians) These oddly formed animals, such as Ciona and Sea Grapes, have the hint of a backbone. They grow on rocks and piling.

1. Ciona **2. Sea Grapes**

FAMILY TREE OF ANIMAL LIFE

At the base of the family tree of animal life are single-celled animals (Protozoa), which still live in warm, shallow seas as they did many millions of years ago. Some build intricate, tiny shells of silica or lime. Sponges are simple or colonial animals. Some kinds, of ancient origin, have "skeletons" of silica; many have the fibrous (spongin) skeletons we all know. Jellyfish and hydroids are a large, complex, and diverse group—some solitary, some colonial. Coral animals build hard, limy walls which gradually make coral rock. The worms, though they look somewhat similar, differ strongly internally and hence are put into several distinct but related groups. Starfish have a peculiar radial pattern of growth and odd adaptations for feeding and moving.

Best known of shore animals are the mollusks. Collectors seek their many, varied shells. The living animals (some of which lack shells) are interesting, too. Detailed identification of shells may require more advanced books (p. 154) or the help of an expert. The jointed-legged animals include such marine groups as crabs, lobsters, and barnacles. Along the shores we still find simple chordates —creatures related to ancestors of backboned animals. We see also shore birds (pp. 147-153) and fishes.

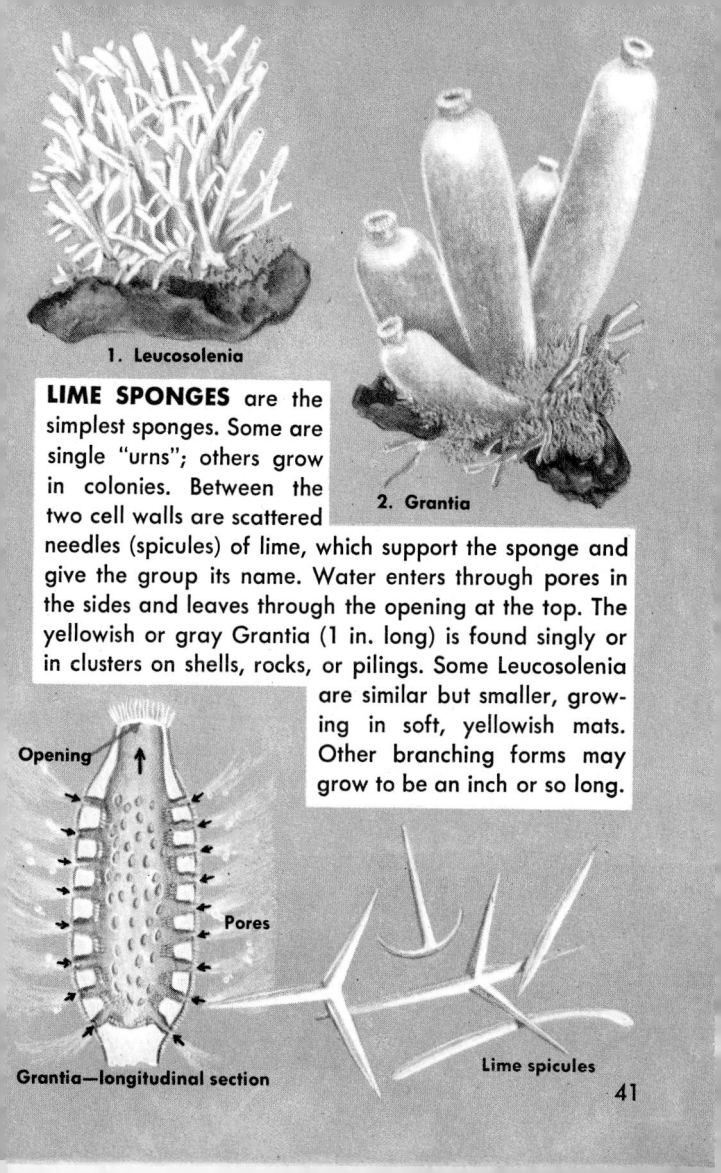

1. Leucosolenia

2. Grantia

LIME SPONGES are the simplest sponges. Some are single "urns"; others grow in colonies. Between the two cell walls are scattered needles (spicules) of lime, which support the sponge and give the group its name. Water enters through pores in the sides and leaves through the opening at the top. The yellowish or gray Grantia (1 in. long) is found singly or in clusters on shells, rocks, or pilings. Some Leucosolenia are similar but smaller, growing in soft, yellowish mats. Other branching forms may grow to be an inch or so long.

Sponge diver

HORNY SPONGES, the best-known kinds, include over 2,000 species. A few live in ponds but most are marine, and common in warmer waters. A boring sponge, Cliona riddles shellfish with tiny holes. Suberites, the Sulfur Sponge, also attaches itself to shells and rocks, where it grows 2 to 3 in. long. Both are shallow-water species. Microciona, or Redbeard Sponge, encrusts shells and pilings. Similar orange and yellow species occur on Atlantic and Pacific coasts. One, Deadman's Fingers (Chalina), is commonly washed up on beaches.

1. Redbeard Sponge

2. Boring Sponge

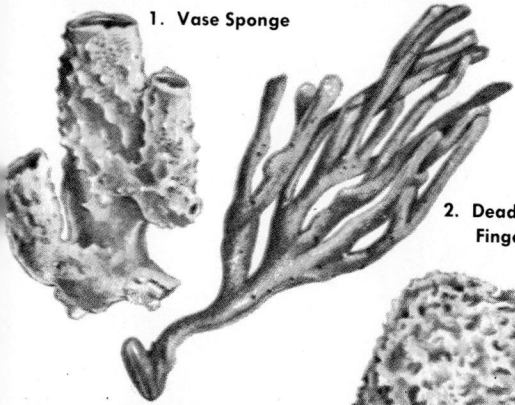

1. Vase Sponge

2. Deadman's Fingers

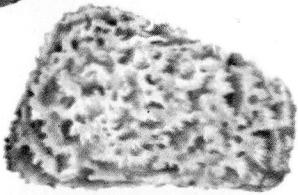

3. Sheep's Wool Sponge

4. Glove Sponge

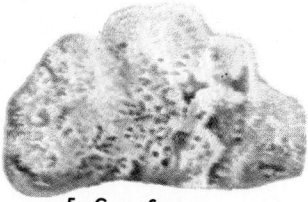

5. Grass Sponge

BATH SPONGES are of several kinds. The glove sponges, horse sponges, and sheep's wool sponges are gathered by divers. They are dried, cleaned, and bleached before they are sold. Tarpon Springs, Florida, is the center for American sponge fishing. The once-important industry has given way to artificial sponges made of cellulose. Other sponges—vase sponges, grass sponges, and dozens more — are found in Gulf waters, growing on the ocean bottom and feeding on small water animals. Sponges can regrow lost or injured parts.

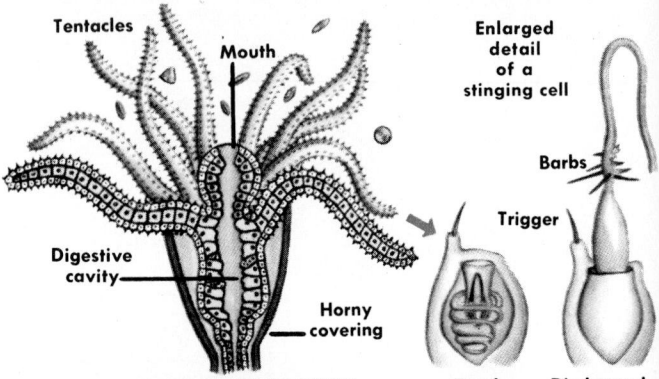

FEEDING POLYP OF OBELIA
(Internal Structure)

POLYP and JELLYFISH ANIMALS (Coelenterates), a diverse group, have a central digestive cavity. Its opening is ringed by stinging tentacles, which stun or kill small prey. Many have both a free-swimming (medusae or jellyfish) and a more fixed (polyp or hydroid) stage. Some are colonial. Coelenterates include Hydrozoa (polyps and medusae, usually small); Scyphozoa (medusae only, fairly large); and Anthozoa (polyps only, usually fairly large).

THREE MAJOR GROUPS OF COELENTERATES

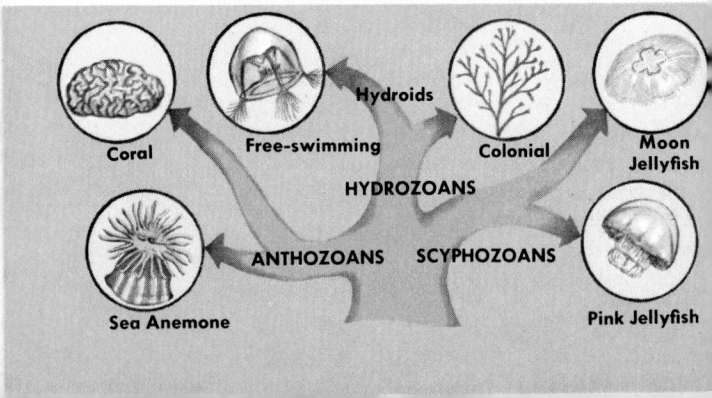

1. Moon Jellyfish 3″-9″ **2. Pink Jellyfish 1′-8′**

JELLYFISH The moon jellyfish, very common, with color varying from white to pink and orange, is washed up on all our beaches. Its milky disc, 3 to 9 in. across, has radiating canals and a thin indented fringe. Tentacles are very short. Pink jellyfish, of colder waters, is larger—1 ft. or more wide, with long, trailing tentacles. Specimens 8 ft. across with tentacles over 100 ft. long are reported. It swims by opening and closing its disc.

COELENTERATES are of many kinds. The Obelias are small colonies (1 to 8 in.) growing on rocks, piles, or seaweeds. Common along the Atlantic Coast, they are found the world over. Note the branching stems which under magnification show both feeding and reproductive polyps. The small, free-swimming medusae have 8 to 24 tentacles. Most Tubularia, unbranched or in small colonies, are common in northern waters. Some are found as far south as Florida. Each hydroid (about ¼ in. or less in diameter) has about two dozen short tentacles. Gonionemus, a New England species, is typical of many free-swimming jellyfish. It is about an inch in diameter, with 60 to 80 tentacles, each less

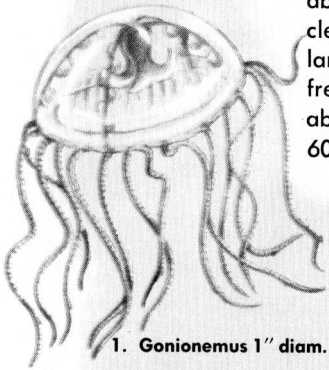

1. Gonionemus 1″ diam.

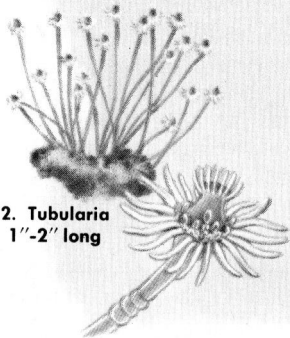

2. Tubularia 1″-2″ long

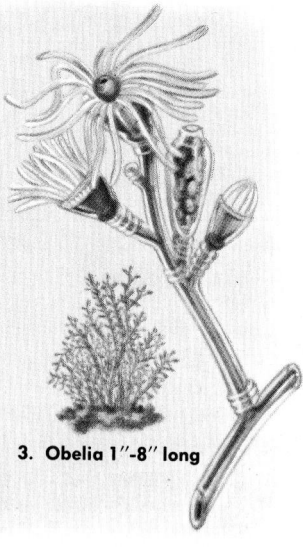

3. Obelia 1″-8″ long

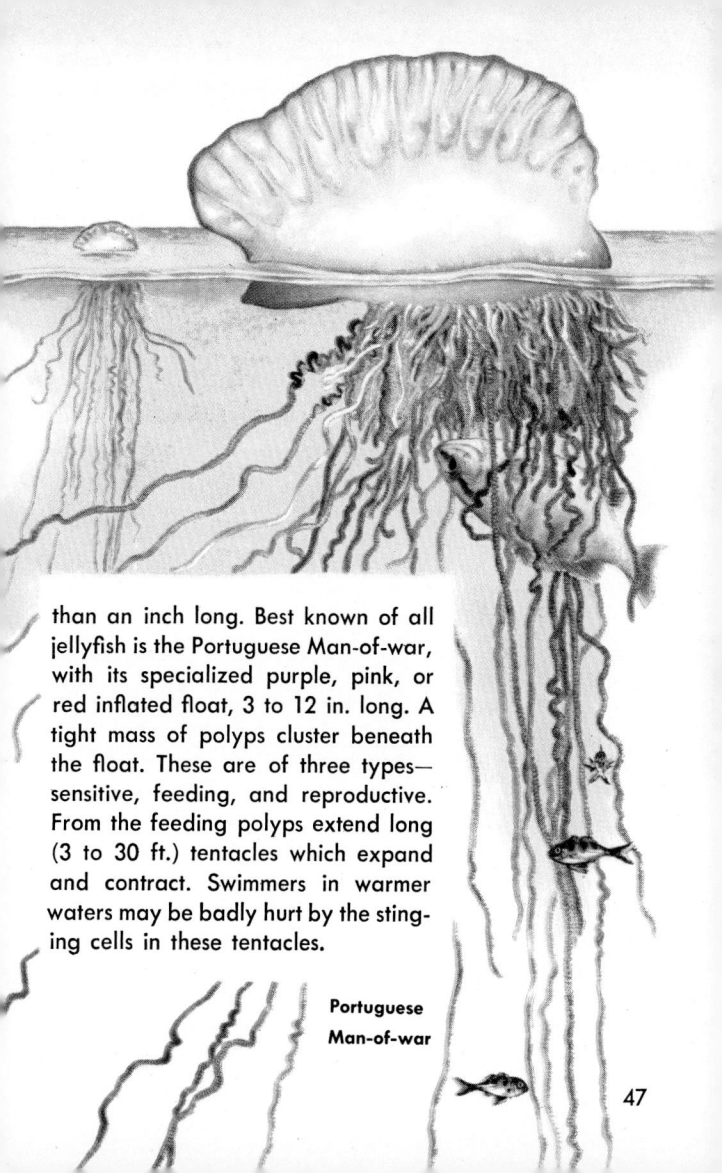

than an inch long. Best known of all jellyfish is the Portuguese Man-of-war, with its specialized purple, pink, or red inflated float, 3 to 12 in. long. A tight mass of polyps cluster beneath the float. These are of three types—sensitive, feeding, and reproductive. From the feeding polyps extend long (3 to 30 ft.) tentacles which expand and contract. Swimmers in warmer waters may be badly hurt by the stinging cells in these tentacles.

Portuguese Man-of-war

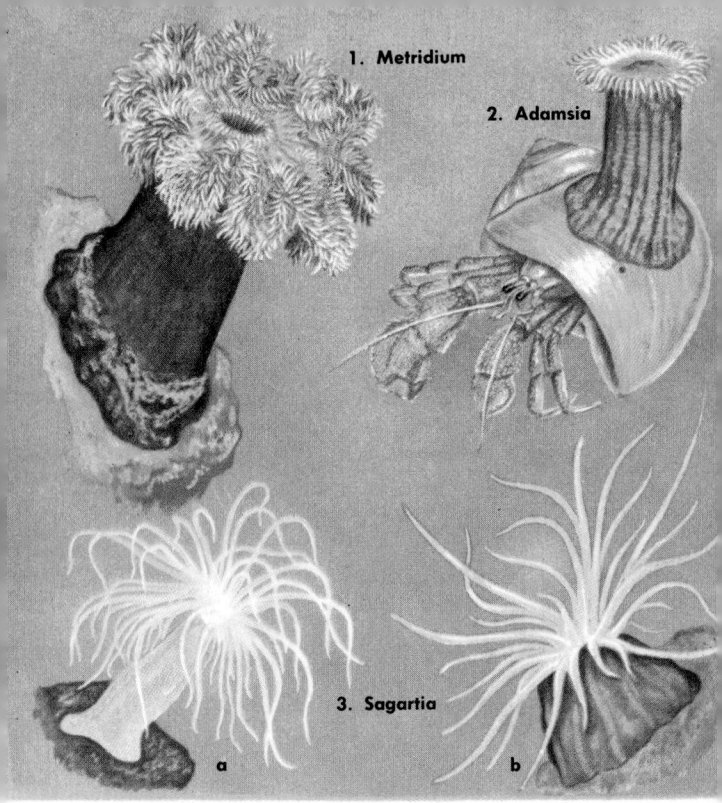

SEA ANEMONES look like flowers, as they grow attached to rocks and piles. The tentacles around the mouth cavity open like fleshy petals, and contract whenever danger threatens. Sea anemones usually do not have a free-swimming jellyfish stage. The fertilized egg grows into a larva, which soon settles down to a fixed existence. Metridium, sometimes 3 in. high, with many white tentacles, is common in northern waters, both Atlantic and Pacific. Several species of Sagartia, about 1 in. high and delicately colored, are also found on both coasts, growing on rocks or in sand near the low-tide mark. The Pacific species, believed to have been introduced with oysters from Japan, is small (½ in.), dark green with orange stripes. Adamsia, an unusual anemone, may grow 3 in. high. It attaches itself to a Hermit Crab's adopted shell (p. 73) and so gets free transportation. It is most common along the South Atlantic Coast. Green Anemone, or Cribrina, occurs abundantly in western tide pools. The color is due to algae, which actually live in the anemone's tissues. Both plant and animal benefit from this odd partnership.

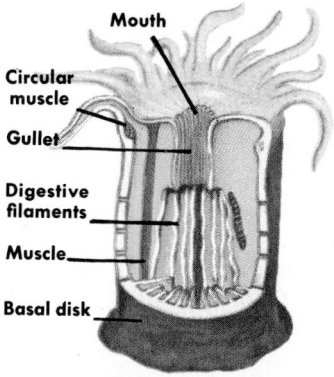

INTERNAL VIEW OF ANEMONE

Green Anemone

1. Balanophylla
0.5″ diam.

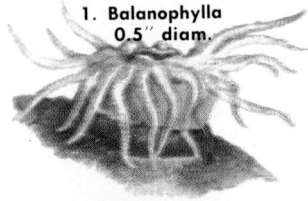

Polyp expanded

Top view of stony cup

2. Astrangia

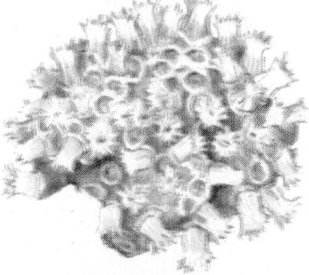

Polyps 0.4″ diam.

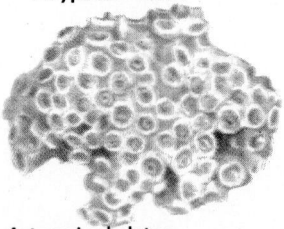

Astrangia skeleton

CORALS, closely related to sea anemones, are of several groups. One has bits of lime imbedded in the body walls but does not produce the typical coral "skeleton." Another (p. 52) makes horny skeletons. The stony corals are best known. These are the corals which form great reefs, atolls, and islands. Cells at the base of each polyp take lime from sea water to build up their skeletons. A few of these corals grow singly; most are colonial, thriving in warm, fairly shallow water. Northern species are washed up on New England beaches, but most corals you will see come from south

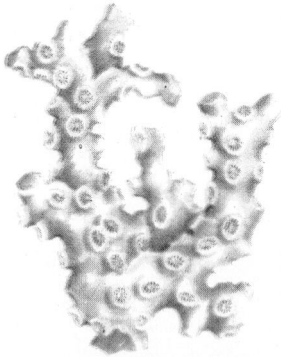

3. Eyed Coral skeleton

1. Precious Coral

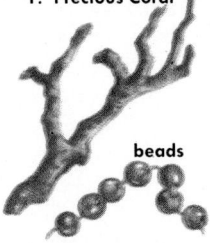

2. Leaf Coral

3. Staghorn Coral

Atlantic and Gulf waters. Two eastern, cooler-water corals are Astrangia and Oculina, both with white skeletons. The three Pacific kinds include Balanophylla, a solitary orange coral, and another Astrangia. Precious Coral comes from the Mediterranean. Similar species have recently been found in deep waters off California. About a dozen corals are common in Florida and West Indian reefs. All have white skeletons. Best known are Brain, Star, and Staghorn.

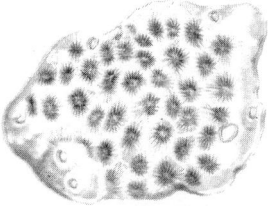

4. Star Coral

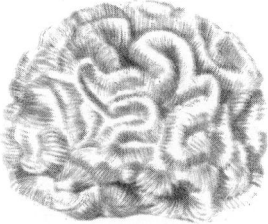

5. Brain Coral

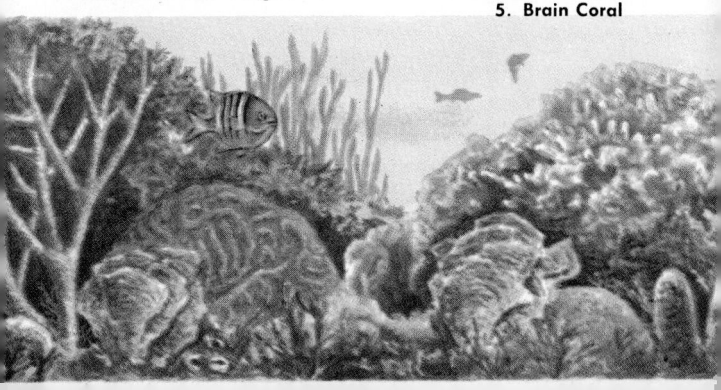

1. Sea Pen 4″

SEA FANS and SEA PENS The former are horny corals including those called Sea Plumes or Sea Whips. Sea Fan is common in warmer waters on both coasts. Polyps are small, with eight tentacles. The flexible, brightly colored dried skeletons are often seen in curio shops. Sea Pens are related animals, named from their odd shape. Found in both Atlantic and Pacific, they grow from 4 in. to over a foot long. Muddy bottoms of some Pacific bays are covered with a common green species of Pennatula. These animals contract when disturbed and seem to disappear.

2. Sea Fan 2′

3. Sea Whip 2′- 4′

1. Venus'Girdle - about 6″

COMB JELLIES were once classified as Coelenterates. Closer study shows that they possess many characteristics which are not common to this large group. They lack stinging cells and typically have only a single pair of tentacles. They swim by movement of eight fringed combplates, using balancing organs to keep them upright in the water. Some Comb Jellies are round or egg-shaped. One, with the long name of Pleurobrachia, has world-wide distribution. Even better known is Venus' Girdle, a ribbon-like form about 6 in. long, which is sometimes abundant along the Atlantic Coast.

2. Pleurobrachia
About 1″ long

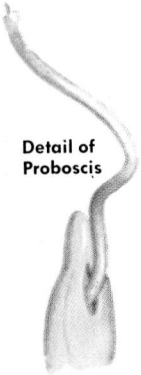

Detail of Proboscis

RIBBON WORMS, mostly marine, 1 in. to about 90 ft., are more advanced than the flatworms, less advanced than the segmented worms. They feed on small marine animals, capturing their food with a proboscis—a contracting tube with a pointed end. Cerebratulus includes the largest American ribbon worms —some up to 20 ft. long. They live in mud and under rocks by day, swimming at night. Color varies from cream or brownish to pink. Ribbon worms are cylindrical or flat; some are red, orange, and purple.

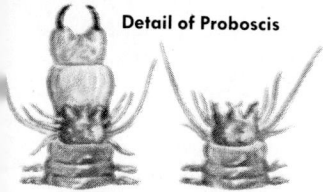

SANDWORMS belong to the group of segmented worms (pp. 56-57), the most advanced of the worm-like animals. Besides the segments, group characteristics include bristled appendages and internal organs arranged symmetrically. Sandworms are found in sand and under rocks along Atlantic and Pacific shorelines. They swim freely at night, especially during the breeding season. Other worms and small sea animals are seized by the sharp, horny jaws and eaten. Some species grow several feet in length. However, these are not as common. The Clam Worm, illustrated here, is the best-known species, found on both eastern and western sides of the north Atlantic. Lives in a thin tube in sand or mud; 12 to 18 in. long.

Male Sandworms are bright blue-green. Females are duller with orange and red.

Clam Worm or Sandworm

Fan Worm

SEGMENTED WORMS, a group of some 8,000 species, include sandworms, leeches, and earthworms. The marine forms are varied, unusual, and may be brightly colored.

Sea Mouse is a broad worm (3 to 6 in. long), covered with long, gray, iridescent "hair." It lives on sandy bottoms in shallow water on both sides of the north Atlantic. A related species has more prominent feeding appendages around the mouth.

Lugworm is a burrowing animal like the earthworm. It lives well below the surface and feeds by extracting organic matter from the fine sand and debris it takes in as it burrows along. Length: 6 to 8 in.

Parchment Worm lives in U-shaped tubes on muddy bottoms. Water is sucked in at one end, bringing oxygen and plankton food. Wastes are discharged at the other. The tube is built of a tough membrane, hence the common name of this worm. Tube openings can be seen dotting the bottom of shallow water at low tide.

Trumpet Worms are small (2 in.), segmented worms, which build their own conical tubes out of grains of sand neatly and attractively cemented together. These sedentary animals use plume-like appendages for respiration and in gathering food, and curved ones to help them dig.

Fringed Worms are unusual-looking creatures about 6 in. long. They are earthworm-like in appearance, except for many long, thin, fleshy appendages growing from most segments. These are exposed and help obtain oxygen for the worm, which lives buried in the mud.

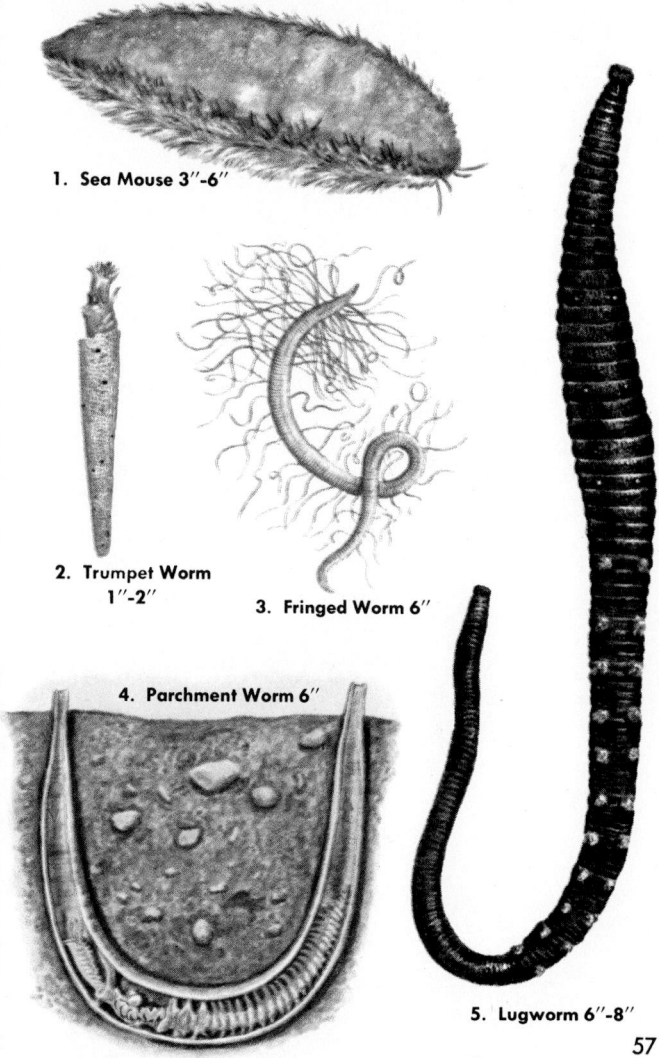

1. Sea Mouse 3″-6″

2. Trumpet Worm 1″-2″

3. Fringed Worm 6″

4. Parchment Worm 6″

5. Lugworm 6″-8″

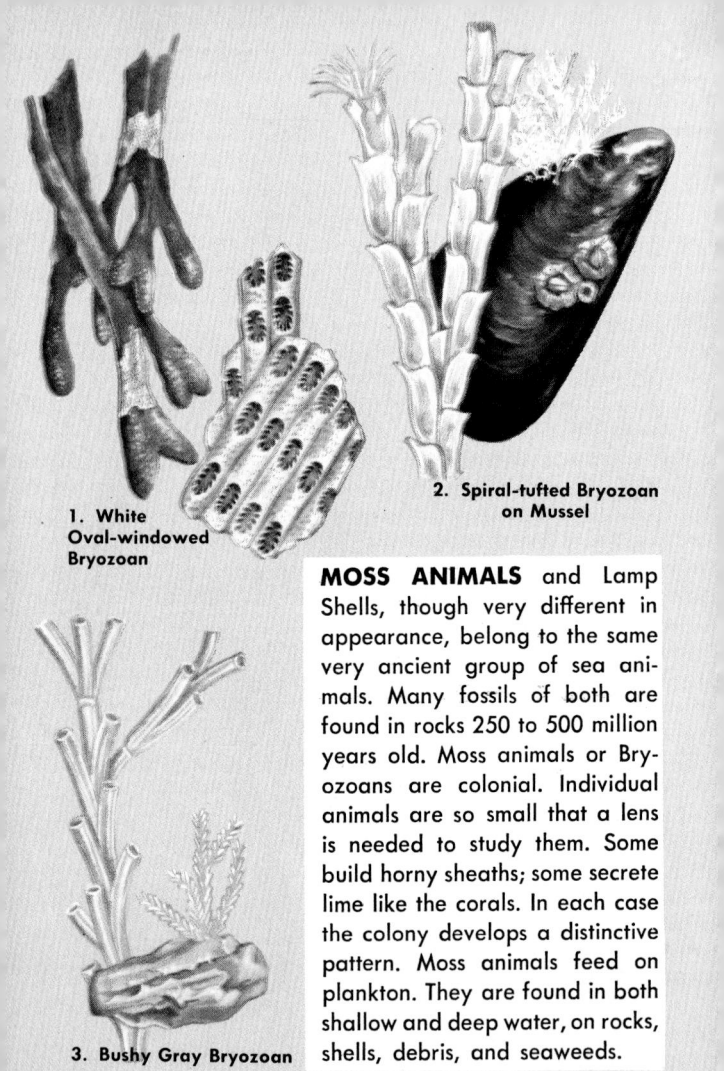

1. White Oval-windowed Bryozoan

2. Spiral-tufted Bryozoan on Mussel

3. Bushy Gray Bryozoan

MOSS ANIMALS and Lamp Shells, though very different in appearance, belong to the same very ancient group of sea animals. Many fossils of both are found in rocks 250 to 500 million years old. Moss animals or Bryozoans are colonial. Individual animals are so small that a lens is needed to study them. Some build horny sheaths; some secrete lime like the corals. In each case the colony develops a distinctive pattern. Moss animals feed on plankton. They are found in both shallow and deep water, on rocks, shells, debris, and seaweeds.

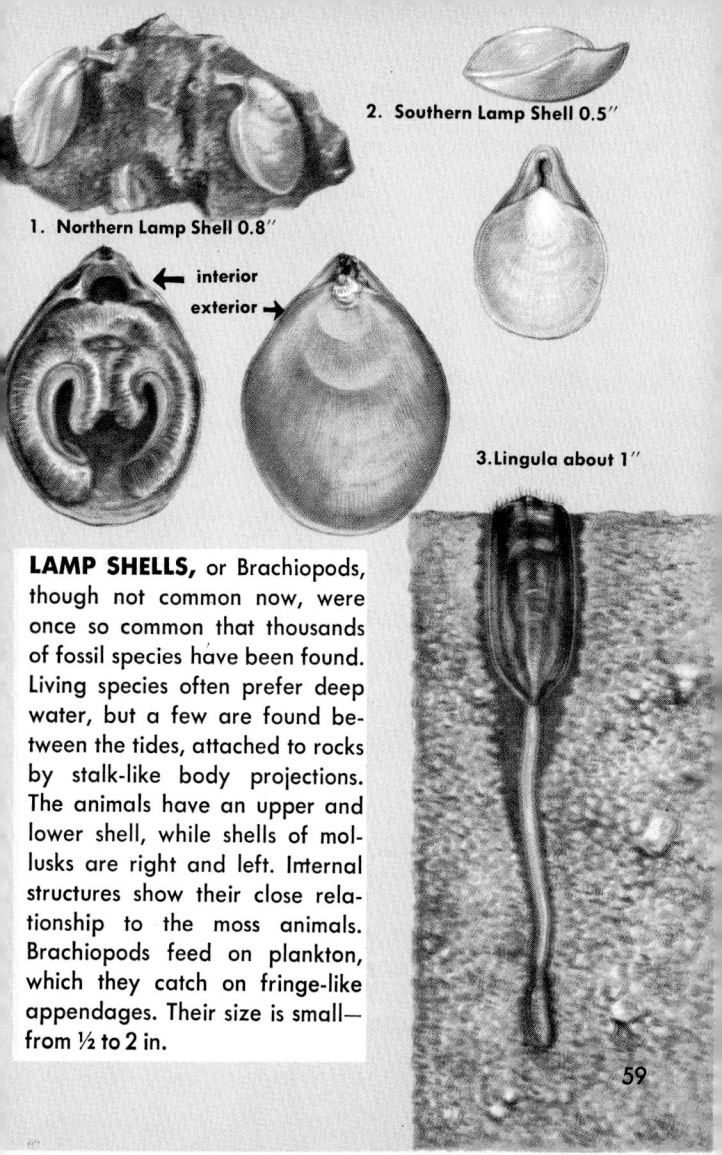

LAMP SHELLS, or Brachiopods, though not common now, were once so common that thousands of fossil species have been found. Living species often prefer deep water, but a few are found between the tides, attached to rocks by stalk-like body projections. The animals have an upper and lower shell, while shells of mollusks are right and left. Internal structures show their close relationship to the moss animals. Brachiopods feed on plankton, which they catch on fringe-like appendages. Their size is small—from ½ to 2 in.

FAMILY TREE OF SPINY-SKINNED ANIMALS

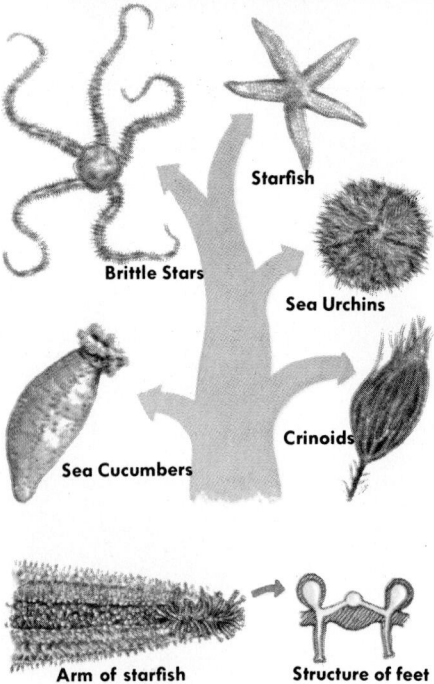

ECHINODERMS are marine animals that have limy plates, often with spines, for "skeletons." The plates may be connected at movable joints, as in some Starfish. They may form a continuous shell, as in the Sea Urchins, or they are not connected at all, as in Sea Cucumbers. Adult Echinoderms exhibit a star-like pattern, some with radiating arms. Small tube feet on these arms grip surfaces, helping the animal to move and obtain food. They connect to a system of internal tubes through which sea water circulates.

1. Snake Star to 3.5″

2. Basket Star 20″-24″

3. Green Brittle Star to 6″

4. Daisy Brittle Star to 8″

5. Spiny Brittle Star to 6″

BRITTLE and BASKET STARS are a lesser group of Starfish. The thin, flexible arms of Brittle Stars (2 to 6 in. long) are at a broad angle to the disc. They lack functional tube feet but can move up and down as well as sideways. Brittle Stars, mainly deep-water species, are occasionally found in tide pools and on rocky shores. Basket Stars have branching arms up to 24 in. long. These coil around rocks or anchor the animal to seaweeds.

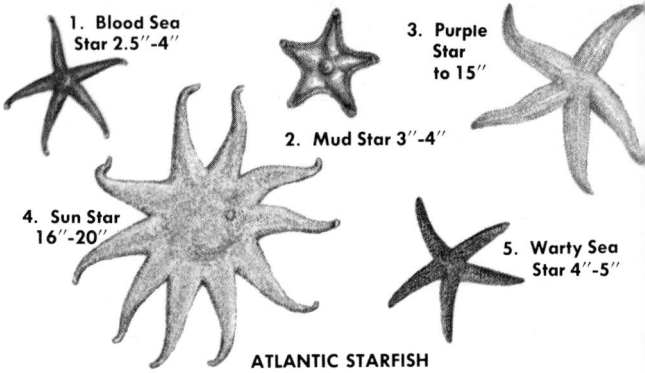

ATLANTIC STARFISH

STARFISH, the best-known Echinoderms, include Brittle and Basket Stars (p. 61) and Starfish or Sea Stars. Common Starfish have arms at a sharp angle to the central disc, which has, on top, a sieve plate. Entering this, water moves through tubes to the tube feet, lying in grooves on the under side of the arms. Arms, 5 to 10 or more, vary

6. Common or Eastern Star 6″-11″

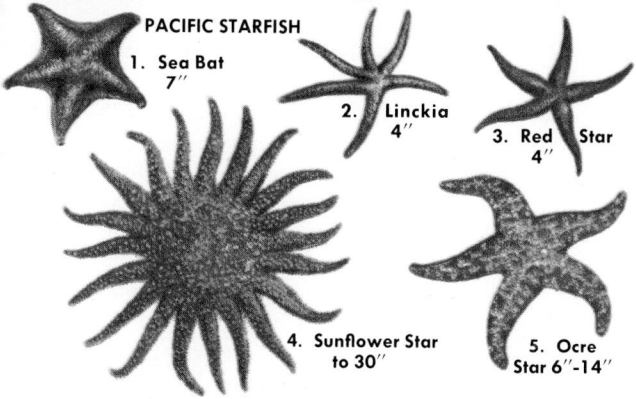

with species; most are spiny, with very tiny pincers amid the spines. Underneath the disc is a mouth. Wrapping its arms over a clam, the starfish uses sustained suction of the tube feet to force it open. Then it extends its stomach through its mouth into the clam shell and digests the clam there. Starfish destroy millions of dollars' worth of shellfish yearly.

Starfish feeding on oyster

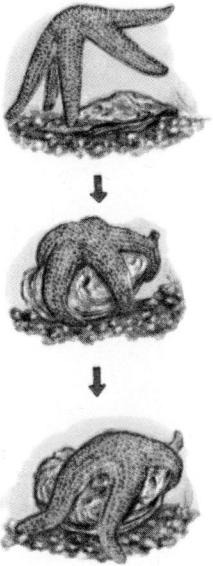

Regeneration of arms

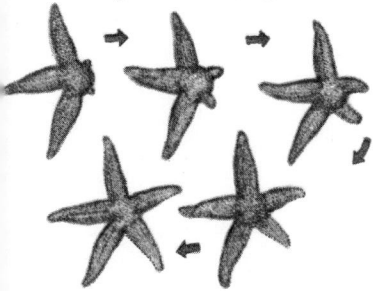

1. Cidaris to 2.5″

SEA URCHINS and SAND DOLLARS are Echinoderms in which the plates are joined to form a firm shell. A five-rayed pattern of pores for the tube feet shows the close relationship to Starfish. Many Sea Urchins live on rocks in shallow water. Those that live in deeper water occur in groups, which sometimes carpet a large area of sea bottom. Live Sea Urchins are covered with movable spines—long, short, delicate, or heavy, depending on the species. Those of some tropical species have around the base of the spines structures which extrude poison. Sea Urchin eggs are eaten in Europe and the West Indies. Sea Urchins range from 1½ to 10 in. in diameter.

Sand Dollars, sometimes called Sea Biscuits, are flattened relatives of the Sea Urchins, with the movable spines greatly reduced in size. The animals live in deeper water, half-buried in sand, feeding on organic material and plankton. Cilia on the spines move these food particles till they are trapped by mucus around the spines and are pushed into the mouth of the animal. A large Pacific starfish feeds on Sand Dollars. Sand Dollar and Sea Urchin "skeletons" are found washed up on beaches.

2. Purple Sea Urchin 1.5″-3″

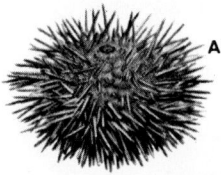

Alive

Dead

3. Sand Dollar 3″

Alive

Dead

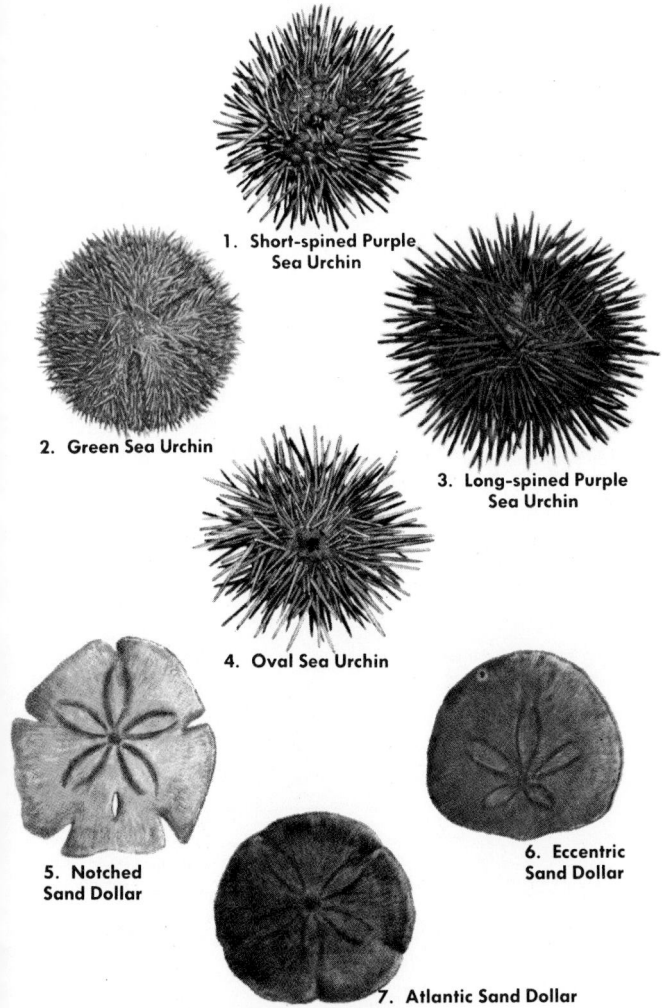

1. Short-spined Purple Sea Urchin

2. Green Sea Urchin

3. Long-spined Purple Sea Urchin

4. Oval Sea Urchin

5. Notched Sand Dollar

6. Eccentric Sand Dollar

7. Atlantic Sand Dollar

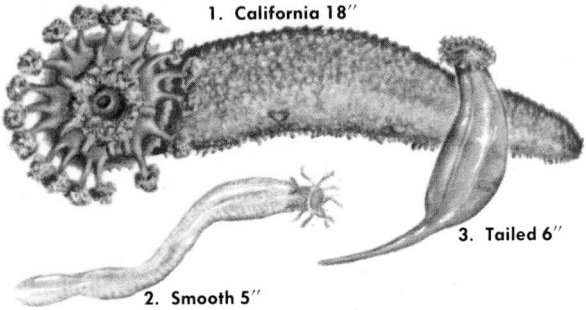

SEA CUCUMBERS are soft or leathery Echinoderms in which the radial pattern is often hard to see. Some are worm-like; some have lost their tube feet. They live buried in sand or under rocks below the low-tide mark and in deeper water. A ring of short-branched tentacles encircles the mouth. Sea Cucumbers range from 2 to 18 in. long and from ½ to 6 in. thick. Some throw out their internal organs when disturbed and regrow them later. Sea Cucumbers are fairly common on both Atlantic and Pacific shores, usually in cooler water.

4. Northern 9″

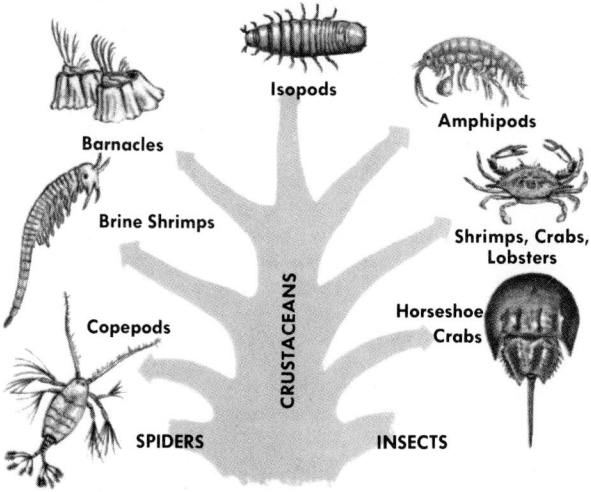

ARTHROPODS

MARINE ARTHROPODS belong almost entirely to the crustaceans, a group of some 25,000 species which, though large, pales beside the insects, a group of over 600,000. Marine crustaceans vary from almost microscopic forms to giants with legs 5 ft. long. Most are small animals. Species of crabs, shrimp, and lobsters are of commercial value. Smaller crustaceans are important foods for many kinds of marine life. All crustaceans have segmented bodies and an external skeleton. Growth involves shedding the old covering and growing a new one. Less conspicuous arthropods, as the copepods, isopods, and amphipods, are important foods for larger marine life and have complex life histories.

ARTHROPODS—over 650,000 kinds

1,000 Other	25,000 Crustaceans	20,000 Spiders	600,000 Insects

1. Gooseneck Barnacles 2″

2. Rock Barnacles to 2″

BARNACLES, shrimp-like in structure, do not look or act like other crustaceans. Eggs hatch into free-swimming larvae, which feed and molt, changing in form as they grow. The new form attaches itself to rocks or timber where, after a resting stage, it becomes a shelled adult. The shell is in divisions which overlap and, when shut, are protective. Modified, feathery feet brush plankton and organic matter into the mouth. Some species resist drying and are found well above the low-tide mark. Ship hulls are treated to prevent drag due to barnacle growths.

SAND HOPPERS (BEACH FLEAS) and their kin form a group of crustaceans which numbers over a thousand species. Most are only a fraction of an inch in length. Some live on the dry beaches, in sand and decaying seaweeds. More kinds live in sand and mud in shallow water. Others are free-swimming. The name of the group—the Amphipods—refers to modified legs for both walking and jumping. These thin, laterally compressed animals have gills at the base of appendages for breathing. Some kinds are so numerous during certain seasons that they form a major part of the plankton. The identification of species is difficult for the amateur. Larger, sand-dwelling species are often dug for bait. The plankton species serve as food for many larger kinds of ocean life.

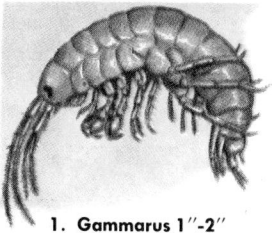

1. Gammarus 1″-2″

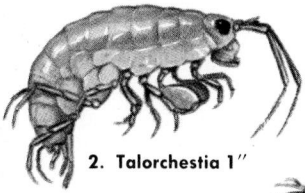

2. Talorchestia 1″

3. California Sand Hopper About 1″

4. Eastern Sand Hopper to 0.5″

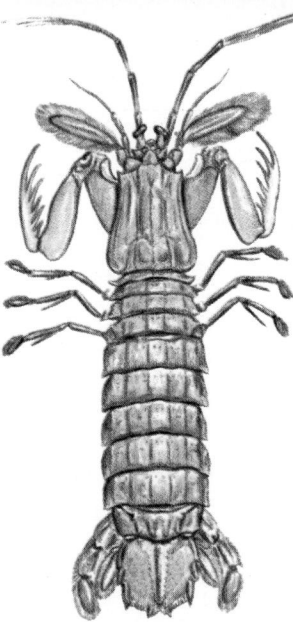

SHRIMPS, lobsters, and crabs, all with five pairs of jointed legs on the thorax plus abdominal appendages, are closely related. The carapace that covers the head and the thorax is fused. Shrimps or Prawns grow up to 9 in. long; most are smaller, and some species are minute. They swim backward with quick strokes of their fan-like tails. The larger shrimps are netted in the Atlantic and Pacific. An important edible species comes from the South Atlantic and Gulf. The Pacific Black-tailed Shrimp also is eaten. Some small shrimp live buried in the mud.

1. Mantis Shrimp (not a true shrimp) to 10″

2. Edible Shrimp 4″-6″

3. Sand Shrimp to 2″

1. American Lobster to 2′

LOBSTERS, a sea-food favorite, live inshore in summer, in deeper water during the winter. Most caught weigh 1 to 3 lb., though older lobsters get much larger. It takes about 5 years for them to grow to edible size. Lobsters, captured in wooden traps baited with dead fish, are now protected as the basis of an important industry. The Spiny Lobster of southern waters and of the Pacific is not a close relative. Also edible, and more colorful, it lacks the large pincers and has a spiny shell.

2. Spiny Lobster 8″-16″

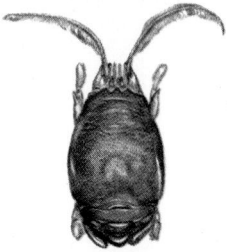

1. Pacific 1″

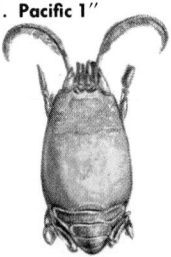

2. Atlantic 1.5″

SANDBUGS, sometimes called Mole Crabs, are known to everyone who has waded in the surf. These common crustaceans live in the sand, moving in and out with the tide. Their heavy, curved carapace disguises their relationship to other crabs. Legs are adapted for digging. Plume-like antennae, held just above the sand, catch organic matter on which these active creatures feed. All movements—swimming, crawling, or digging—are made backward. Females, much larger than males, carry their orange eggs several months before they hatch.

Digging and feeding

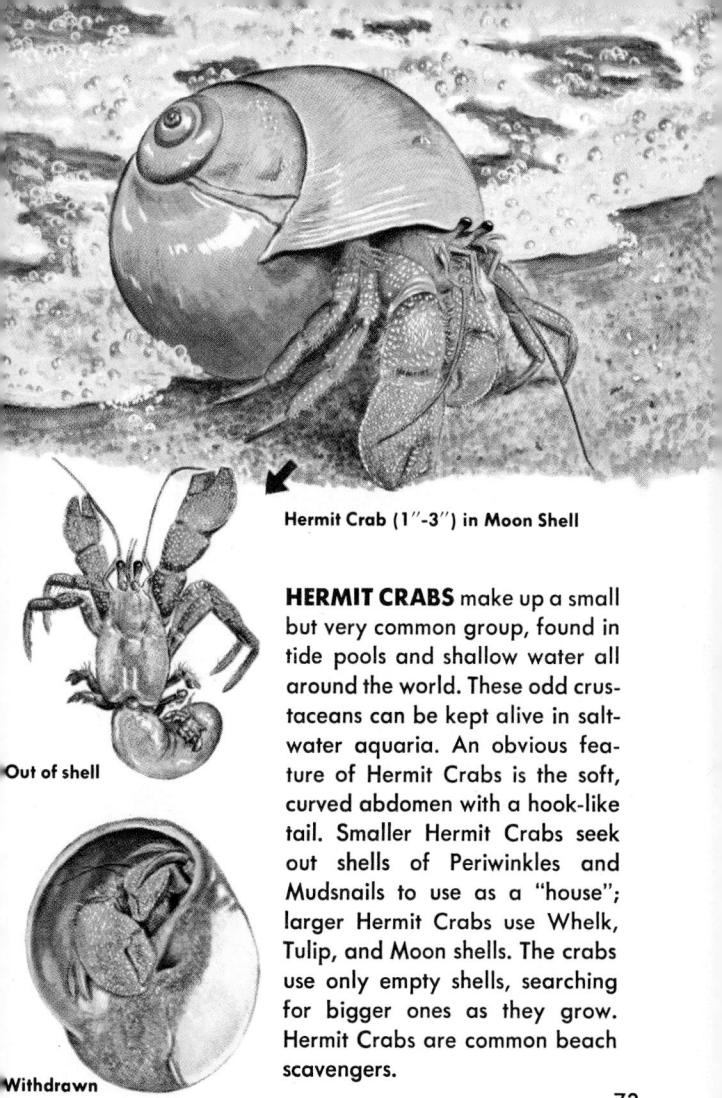

Hermit Crab (1″-3″) in Moon Shell

Out of shell

Withdrawn

HERMIT CRABS make up a small but very common group, found in tide pools and shallow water all around the world. These odd crustaceans can be kept alive in saltwater aquaria. An obvious feature of Hermit Crabs is the soft, curved abdomen with a hook-like tail. Smaller Hermit Crabs seek out shells of Periwinkles and Mudsnails to use as a "house"; larger Hermit Crabs use Whelk, Tulip, and Moon shells. The crabs use only empty shells, searching for bigger ones as they grow. Hermit Crabs are common beach scavengers.

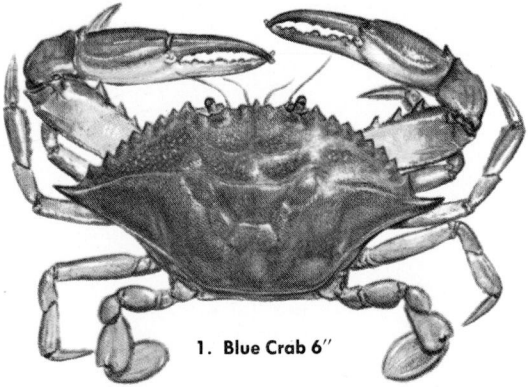

1. Blue Crab 6″

SWIMMING CRABS are a family in which the last pair of legs is flattened and adapted for swimming. Best known in this group is the Blue Crab, prized as sea food all along the Atlantic and Gulf coasts, especially in Chesapeake Bay, which is noted for them. Eggs, laid in summer, remain attached to the body of the female. They hatch in about two weeks as larvae, which are very unlike the adults. The young crabs molt and shed their shells as they grow, and soon assume adult form. They are mature in about a year. After molting, the shell is soft, and crabs caught at this time are sold as soft-shelled crabs, but they are not a different species, as some people may think.

2. Green Crab 3″

Blue Crabs are scavengers which prefer brackish water near mouths of rivers, moving into deeper water in winter. Their number may vary considerably from year to year. Other members of the swimming crab group are smaller and have less value, but all are active, attractive animals, alert and aggressive. The Green Crab does not have its legs modified as much for swimming. The Calico or Lady Crab has a varied, speckled pattern, with a shell about as long as it is broad. It prefers sandy beaches and is sometimes caught for food in the South. Portunus Crabs, which are found on both Atlantic and Pacific coasts, include some smaller species which are usually found on seaweeds.

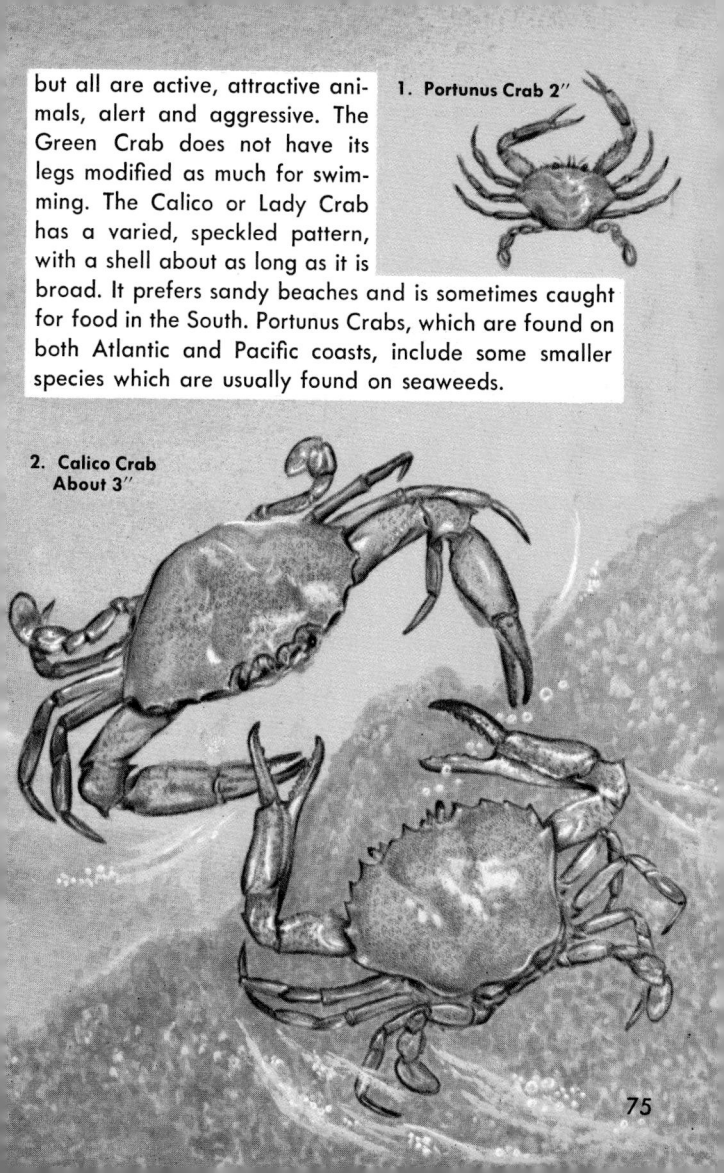

1. Portunus Crab 2″

2. Calico Crab
About 3″

1. Rock

2. Jonah

3. Edible

ROCK CRABS, despite their name, live on sandy bottoms as well as on rocky beaches. On the Pacific Coast, one crab of this group—the Big Crab—grows over a foot across and is caught for market. The crabs prefer cooler waters; they grow larger along the northern shores of both coasts. On the Atlantic Coast are several smaller related species (3 to 4 in.). Young are often found in tide pools. Larger crabs prefer deeper water. Species differ in markings. All have an oval carapace with teeth along the edge.

1. Fiddler Crabs

FIDDLER and SAND CRABS are both burrowing crabs, preferring the drier parts of sandy beaches and salt marshes. Both run rapidly with a sidewise motion. The Fiddler Crab is named after the male's huge single claw, which is seldom used except in mating-season battles. These little crabs dig burrows up to 3 ft. long. They feed on organic material in the sand. The Sand or Ghost Crab lives in even drier sand than the Fiddler. Its protective coloring and quick movements make it seem to disappear right before your eyes.

2. Sand Crabs

1. Kelp Crab

2. Nine-spined Spider Crab

3. Six-spined Spider Crab

SPIDER and KELP CRABS are closely related. Both have long, thin legs, and a shell more rounded than in swimming crabs. Spider Crabs, which are sluggish, have a carapace usually covered with algae, barnacles, and occasionally a Sea Anemone. A number of species are found in shallow water on both Atlantic and Pacific shores. The Kelp Crabs of the Pacific, with cleaner carapace than other Spider Crabs, are found in kelp beds and in tide pools. With their long, agile legs they easily nip an unwary collector.

1. Eurypterid

Male

Female

HORSESHOE or KING CRABS are not crabs at all but may be descendants of ancient Eurypterids which flourished some 400 million years ago. Their nearest living relatives are the spiders. These awkward animals, found along Atlantic beaches, may be very common there. None occur along the West Coast. Though bathers are sometimes frightened by them, Horseshoe Crabs are harmless. The female (up to 20 in.) is larger than the male. Eggs are deposited in sand close to shore. The young live out in deeper water, molting periodically as they grow.

2. Horseshoe Crab to 20″

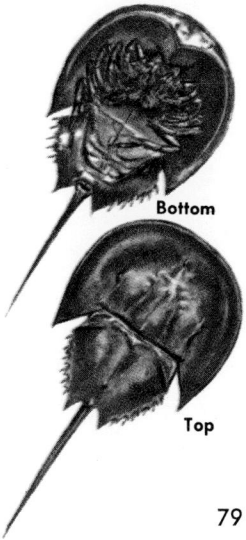

CHITONS p. 81

Bivalves

Squid and Octopus

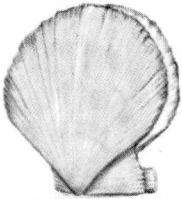

BIVALVES pp. 82-110

Tusk Shells

Sea Snails

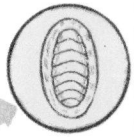

Chitons

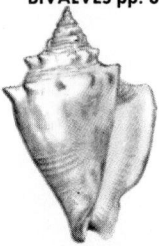

SEA SNAILS
pp. 111-137

SQUID and KIN
pp. 138-139

TUSK SHELLS
p. 140

MOLLUSKS are one of the oldest and largest groups of animals. For over half a billion years species of mollusks have been common in the seas. Some kinds live in fresh water, a few on land. In all, about 100,000 species of mollusks are known, ranging from scarcely visible sea snails to giant squid over 50 ft. long. Five classes of mollusks are illustrated at the left. These animals furnish pearls, buttons, ornaments, and food for man, fish, and other sea animals.

CHITONS are the most primitive mollusks. Their eight overlapping plates will identify them. The margin of the animal may be smooth, hairy, or spiny. A powerful muscular foot holds the Chiton to rocks in tide pools or in shallow water. Most prefer darkness and stay on the underside of the rocks, where they feed on diatoms and other small algae. Over a hundred species are found along the Pacific Coast; fewer along the Atlantic, generally in cooler water. Sizes: ⅓ to 1½ in. and longer.

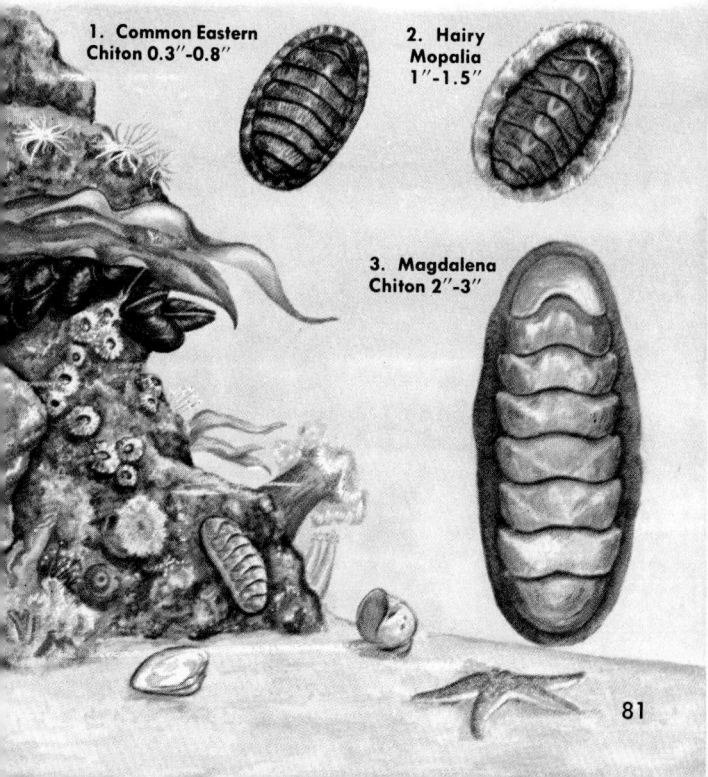

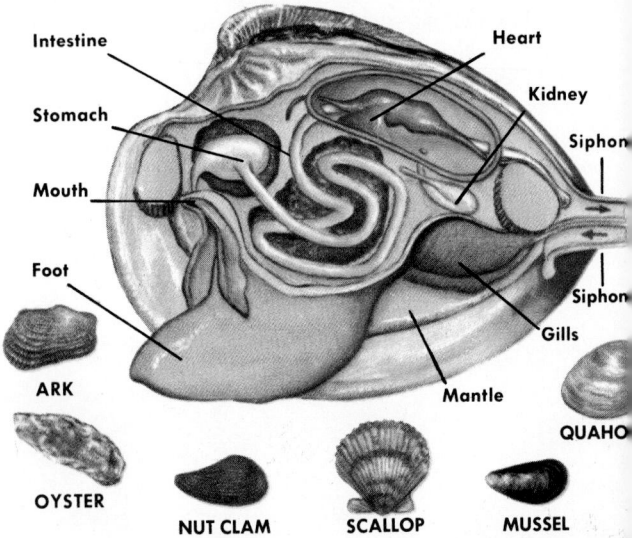

BIVALVES or PELECYPODS are two-shelled mollusks which total about 15,000 species, in about 70 families. Most are marine, though about one-fifth live in fresh water. The two bivalve shells are joined at a hinge. One or two powerful muscles hold the shells together, relaxing to allow the siphons to extend. Water enters through one of these paired tubes, bringing oxygen and food to the bivalve. Water leaves through the other siphon, carrying out waste products.

Bivalves are diverse in form. Some can swim. Some bore in rock. Most live in sand or mud. These may move by means of a muscular "foot," which is thrust forward and anchored. The animal pulls itself forward as the "foot" is contracted. The animal itself is well developed, with gills for breathing and a heart, liver, kidney, and digestive and reproductive systems. The mantle, a soft membrane around the animal, builds the shells out of lime.

NUT CLAMS are a large group of small shells. They are actually three related groups —Acila, Nucula, and Nuculana —found on both coasts with a number of widely distributed arctic species. Several are so common that they can be picked up by the handful. A few others are rarely washed ashore. Fishes and diving ducks feed on these bivalves.

1. Atlantic Nut Clam 0.3″

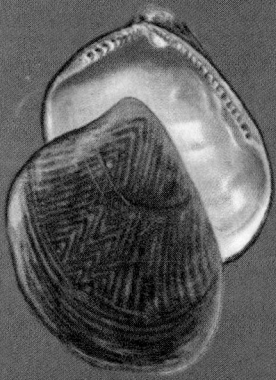

2. Divaricate Nut Clam 0.5″

3. Minute Nut Clam 0.5″

4. Taphria Nut Clam 0.3″-0.8″

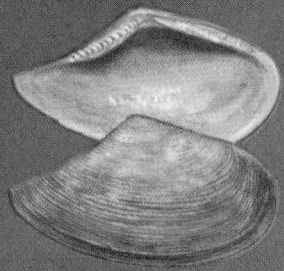

5. Pointed Nut Clam 0.3″-0.4″

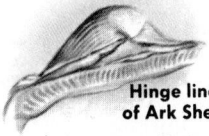

Hinge line of Ark Shell

ARK SHELLS are widely distributed, heavy-shelled animals, more common along the Atlantic than on the Pacific. One, the Blood Ark, of shallow sandy bottoms, is the only common mollusk with red blood. Its shell is marked by strong radiating ribs. Another species with prominent ribs is the Eared Ark of the south California shores. Turkey Wing or Noah's Ark, found on the south Atlantic and Gulf shores, is brightly colored when fresh. Ark Shells also include a number of miniature species. All Arks have a long, narrow, toothed hinge line.

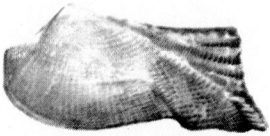

1. **Mossy Ark 1.5″-2.5″**

2. **Blood Ark 1.5″-2.4″**

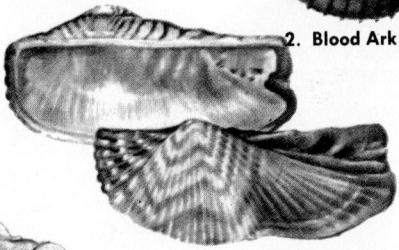

3. **Turkey Wing 2″-3″**

4. **Eared Ark 3″-4″**

5. **Baily's Miniature Ark 0.3″**

Blue Mussels on piling

1. Blue Mussel 1″-3″

2. Atlantic Ribbed Mussel 2″-4″

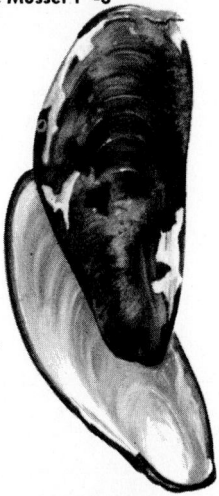

3. Northern Horse Mussel 2″-6″

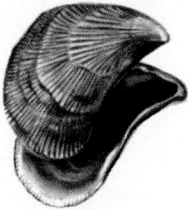

4. Hooked Mussel 1″-2.5″

MUSSELS, widespread in cooler seas, are a favorite food in Europe, but they are not prized here as such. Over a dozen species are found in sand or mud, or attached to rocks and pilings by strong threads (byssus). The Blue Mussel (3 in.) is very common. The Hooked Mussel, smaller (1½ in.), is found farther south. The Horse Mussel (2 to 6 in.) is a deep-water species. Similar kinds are found along the Pacific Coast. These may be poisonous when they feed on dinoflagellates.

SCALLOPS or PECTENS—common, colorful, and appealing in design—delight collectors. Rows of tiny eyes along the edge of the mantle make them unique among bivalves. They are jet-propelled. As their valve opens, the space fills with water. The powerful muscle contracts and the valves pull shut, shooting the water out behind and sending the scallop forward. This large muscle is edible. Most scallops prefer shallow water. Shells are washed up on beaches by storms. Detailed identification involves counting ribs, noting size, color, and the wings which project at the hinge. Scallops are more common along the Atlantic than on the Pacific shores. They vary in size from 1 to 6 in. or more.

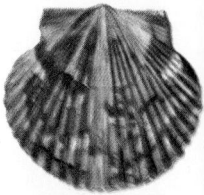

1. Calico Scallop 1″-2″

2. Ornate Scallop 1″-1.3

3. Giant Rock Scallop 8

1. Pacific Pink Scallop 2″-2.8″

2. Kelp-weed Scallop 1″

3. Sentis Scallop 1″-1.5″

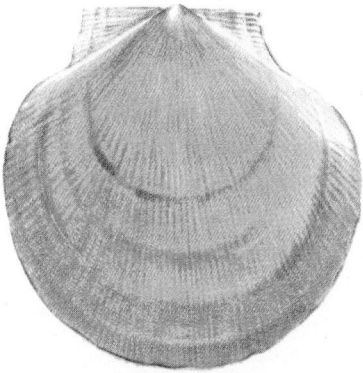

4. Atlantic Deep-sea Scallop 5″-8″

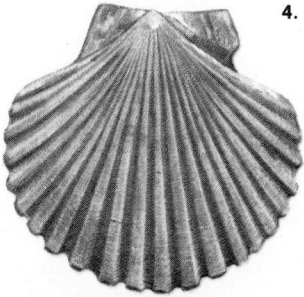

5. San Diego Scallop 3″

6. Atlantic Bay Scallop 2″

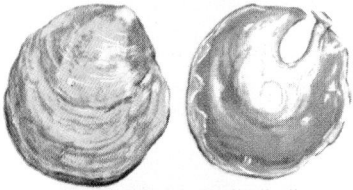

1. Common Jingle Shell 1″-2″

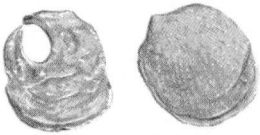

2. Prickly Jingle Shell to 0.8″

3. Peruvian Jingle Shell 1″-2″

JINGLE SHELLS, thin, bright, and pearly, are very common on both coasts, mainly in warmer waters. The shells, about 1 in. across, are unequal, the top one being deeply hollowed, the bottom one smaller and almost flat. The animal anchors itself permanently to rocks, seaweeds, or old shells by a fleshy appendage (byssus) passing through a hole in the lower valve. Only the upper valve is usually washed ashore.

OYSTERS, the most valuable shellfish, are common in shallow, warmer waters of all oceans. The shells are irregular in shape; the valves, unequal in size. When young, oysters are free-swimming; later they attach themselves to shells, rocks, or roots. Most species of oyster are too small to be used as food, though they are eaten by land and other marine animals.

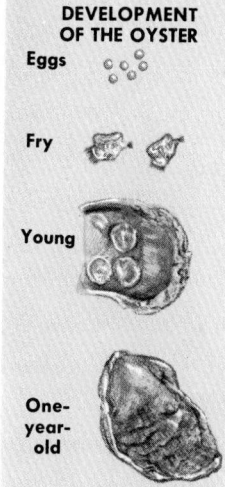

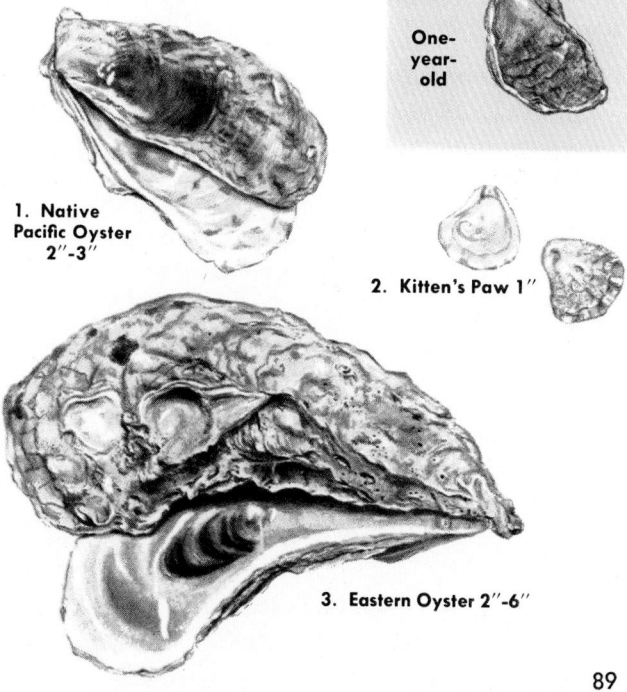

1. Native Pacific Oyster 2″-3″

2. Kitten's Paw 1″

3. Eastern Oyster 2″-6″

1. Saw-toothed Pen Shell 5″-9″

2. Stiff Pen Shell 5″-9″

PEN SHELLS or SEA PENS are large, wedge-shaped shells. The animals grow 4 in. to almost 1 ft. long. Their large muscle, like that of a scallop, is sometimes used for food. Pen Shells prefer warmer, deeper water, where they grow attached to rocks. They are quite rare on the Pacific Coast, though three species are common in the Atlantic. The shells are thin and fragile, dull-colored and rough. The insides are smooth and pearly.

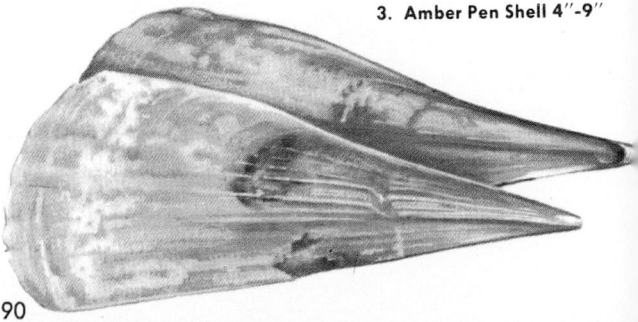

3. Amber Pen Shell 4″-9″

1. Atlantic Wing Oyster 1.5″-3″

WING and PEARL OYSTERS are widespread in warmer waters. The Great Pearl Oyster, source of most pearl and mother-of-pearl, is a large (12 in.) tropical animal. Pearls are found in shells over 5 years old. Cultured pearls are produced by placing balls of shell under the mantle of Pearl Oysters. Only one eastern and one western species of the Wing Oyster are found in our waters. The same holds true for the Pearl Oysters.

2. Pacific Pearl Oyster 1.5″-3″

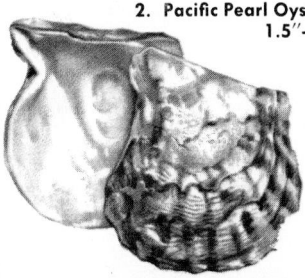

2. Say's Pandora 0.8″-1″

1. Gould's Pandora 0.8″-1.4″

4. Western Pandora 1″

3. Punctate Pandora 2″

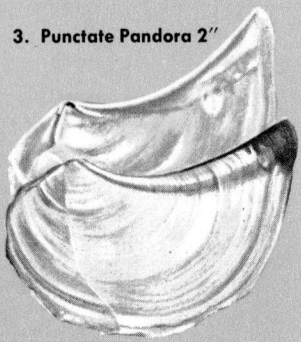

PANDORA SHELLS include over six common species found on both the Atlantic and Pacific coasts. They may occur below the low-tide mark or are dredged up from moderately shallow waters. Pandoras are small shells, rarely over 1½ in. long, usually shorter. The shells are thin, with unequal flattened valves. The right valve is much more flattened than the left. Their color is white, sometimes chalky, and a pearly under-layer may be revealed when the shell is worn. A strong ridge along the hinge line is characteristic. The hinge is toothed. Gould's Pandora, often found from North Carolina northward to Labrador, has a pair of purplish fringed siphons. The Lyonsias and Thracias are related groups, the former somewhat smaller and the latter usually larger than Pandoras. Conrad's Thracia (3 to 4 in.) has a rounded shell with the ridge along the hinge line not strongly developed.

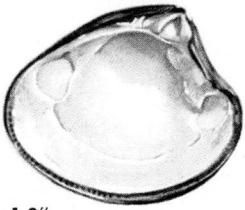

1. Waved Astarte 1.3″

2. Smooth Astarte 1″

3. Striate Astarte 0.5″

ASTARTES, also known as Chestnut Clams, are commonly washed up on beaches. The animals live in shallow or moderately deep water. Their tissues are of a red or orange color. Astartes are small (from ½ to 2 in.), roughly triangular, with a heavy shell. The concentric grooves and ridges are strong in some species. These animals live in cooler waters, north to the Arctic, but two kinds occur as far south as Florida.

4. Alaska Astarte 1″

5. Esquimalt Astarte 0.5″

1. Florida Lucina 1.5″

2. Western Ringed Lucina 2″-2.5″

3. Tiger Lucina 2.5″-3.5″

4. Pennsylvania Lucina 1″-2″

LUCINA or WHITE SHELLS are members of a tropical family common in warmer waters along both Atlantic and Pacific shores. They live on sandy or muddy bottoms in shallow water or moderate depths. Shells are rough, ½ to 3½ in. across, usually white. The surface may be ridged, and some species have a deep fold running from the tip of the shell to the margin. Eggs are sometimes retained within the gill chamber while they develop.

COCKLE or HEART SHELLS are close relatives of the edible Cockle of Europe. All the shells are heart-shaped, with strong radiating ribs. Valves are of equal size. The animals live in sand and mud. They prefer shallow water, often in brackish inlets. The Iceland Cockle (2½ in.) is found in cooler waters of both oceans. The Yellow Cockle (2 in.), yellowish with brown, has 30 to 40 ribs. It occurs south from the Carolinas. Nuttall's Cockle (3 to 6 in.) is an abundant Pacific species; white or yellow with strong squarish ribs. The Giant Atlantic Cockle (3 to 5 in.) has 30 to 36 ribs, and the margins of its valves are toothed. It is a common animal along the south Atlantic and Gulf coasts.

1. Iceland Cockle 2.5″

2. Yellow Cockle 2″

3. Nuttall's Cockle 3″-6″

4. Giant Atlantic Cockle 3″-5″

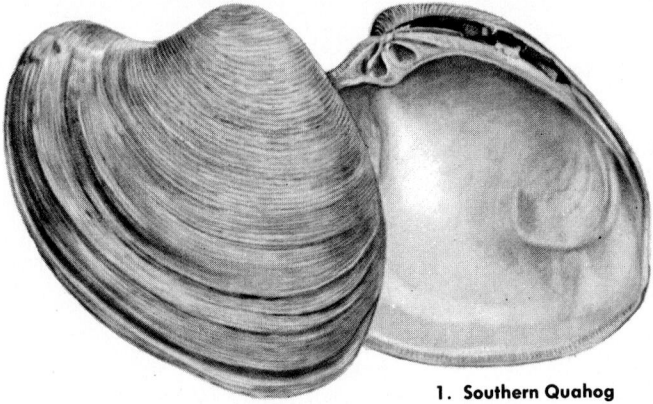

1. Southern Quahog

QUAHOGS or HARD-SHELL CLAMS are a small but important group of bivalves. Related tropical forms are beautifully shaped and marked. The typical Atlantic Coast species (3 to 5 in.), called Quahog by the Indians and also Littleneck or Cherrystone Clams (for small sizes), is less attractive but more appetizing. It was used as food by the Indians and has been eaten ever since, fresh and in chowders. The Southern Quahog is larger, with a heavier shell. Both are found in sand or mud near the low-tide mark. The coastal Indians made wampum from the

2. Northern Quahog with foot and siphons extended

Northern Quahog

Section of William Penn wampum belt

white and purple parts of the Quahog shell. Purple wampum was highly prized. The shells were broken, drilled, and rubbed down to make beads about ¼ in. long. These were strung in short strands or woven into belts. Wampum belts served to bind treaties; shorter strings were used in trade.

Wampum beads (enlarged)

1. Thin-shelled Littleneck about 4″

2. Common Pacific Littleneck 1.5″-2″—two forms

ROCK VENUS SHELLS, or LITTLENECKS, are Pacific species that include the commonest clams of the Pacific Coast. Common Pacific Littleneck (1½ to 2 in.) is the hard-shell clam of sandy bottoms, most common north of San Francisco. It occurs in several forms or varieties. One of these, the Rough-sided Littleneck (up to 3 in.), more common to the south, is marked by prominent lines on the shell. The Thin-shelled Littleneck is a large species (about 4 in.), relatively flatter, with fewer markings and light grayish brown in color.

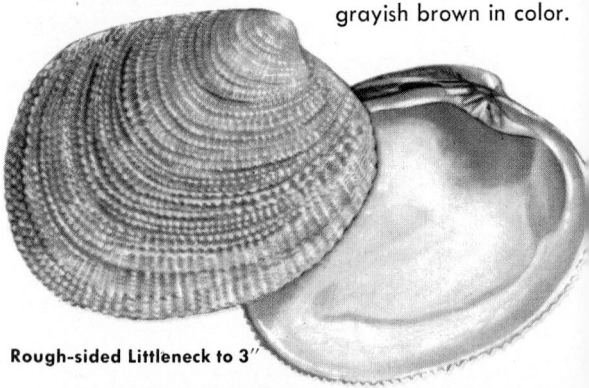

3. Rough-sided Littleneck to 3″

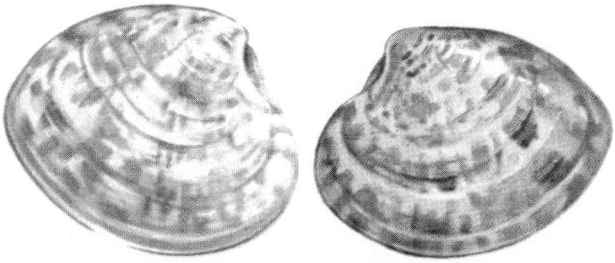

1. Calico Clam 1.5″-2.5″

CALICO CLAMS are attractive, clam-like animals of the south Atlantic and Gulf coasts. The Sunray Venus or Sunray Shell, best known in this group (up to 5 in. long), is pink, gray, and lavender. Interior is pink. The animal lives in sand just below the tide mark. The smaller Calico Clam (1½ to 2½ in.) is known also as the Checkerboard, from the square, brownish spots on the thick, smooth valves. The interior is white. This species occurs south of the Carolinas and is especially common on Florida west-coast shores.

2. Sunray Venus 4″-5″

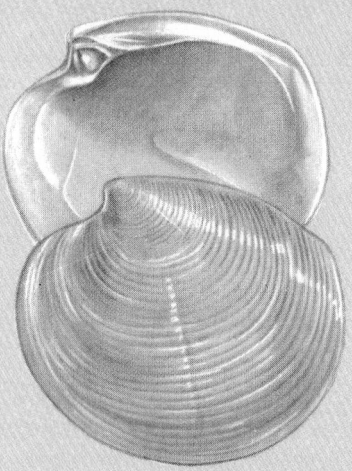

1. Elegant Dosinia 2″-3″

2. Disc Dosinia 2″-3″

AMETHYST GEM CLAM and DOSINIA are both Atlantic Coast shells. The first is a small (¼ in.), pea-sized, smooth shell found commonly on northern beaches. Exterior, lavender to purple; interior, paler. Common from New Jersey south. This small clam has been introduced with oysters into Puget Sound. Closely related are two species of Dosinia. Both have thin, shiny, white, circular shells 2 to 3 in. long. The more common kind has a fine, yellowish skin over the white shell. Dosinias live in sand in shallow southern waters.

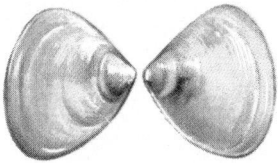

3. Amethyst Gem Clam 0.3″

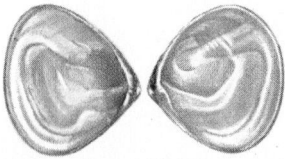

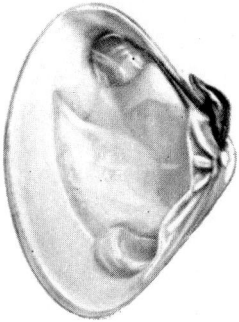

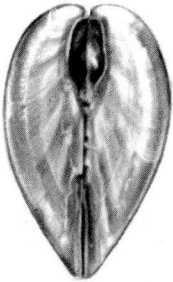

PISMO CLAMS, famous for their flavor, are found on open, sandy beaches from mid-California south. Commercial digging has so reduced the number of Pismo Clams that the law permits a person to dig only 15 clams daily. Even so, there is danger of their disappearing from California beaches. The thick, smooth, gray to brown shells are almost triangular. Pismo Clams take 4 to 7 years to grow 5 in. (present legal minimum for digging), but they may continue to grow more slowly for another 10 years.

1. **Bodega Tellin to 2″**

2. **Carpenter's Tellin 0.4″**

3. **Sunrise Tellin 2″-4″**

4. **Salmon Tellin 0.5″**

5. **Modest Tellin 0.8″-1″**

6. **Speckled Tellin 2.5″-3.5″**

7. **Rose Petal Tellin 1.5″**

TELLIN SHELLS belong to a family which is often considered the aristocracy of the bivalves. Of several hundred species, a score and more are found along our coasts, especially in the warmer waters of the Atlantic and Gulf. Tellin Shells are diverse in size (¼ to 4 in.), but all are relatively thin and compressed. The hinge is not strong, and shells washed up on the beach are often broken apart.

The shells are delicately colored—white, yellow, pink, and purple—varying with the individuals and species. On the Pacific Coast look for the Modest, Salmon, and Carpenter's Tellins. The South Atlantic Coast has a greater variety and includes such well-known kinds as the Sunrise Tellin, Dwarf Tellin, Tampa Tellin, and Rose Petal Tellin.

1. Tenta Macoma 0.5″-0.8″

3. Constricted Macoma 1″-2.5″

2. Balthic Macoma 0.5″-1.5″

4. White Sand Macoma 2″-4″

MACOMA SHELLS are another widespread group, larger than the Tellins and not as attractive. These thin, glossy shells are usually white, but are sometimes covered with a thin, brownish membrane. While some species live in cooler water, others extend far into the tropics. They tend to favor muddy bottoms in protected waters.

5. Indented Macoma 1.5″

6. Bent-nose Macoma 2″-3.5″

1. Denticulate Donax 1″

3. California Donax to 1″

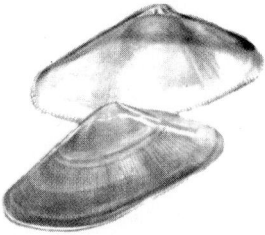

2. Fossor Donax to 0.5″

4. Gould's Donax 0.8″

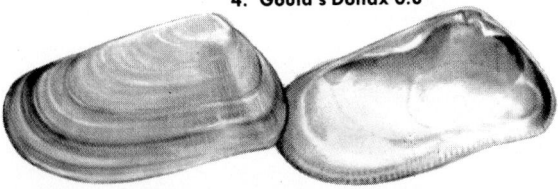

COQUINA, DONAX, or WEDGE SHELLS live in sand close to shore in warm waters of the Atlantic, Pacific, and Gulf. Some kinds are so abundant that, despite their small size, they are dug to make chowder. Along the South Atlantic the Coquina is also called Pompano Shell and Butterfly Shell. The last name refers to the fact that valves, washed ashore, often remain attached but spread open like butterfly wings. All Donax shells show great variation in color and markings. A handful picked up at random will illustrate this.

5. Coquina 0.5″-0.8″

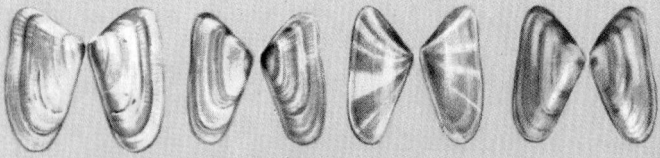

1. Rosy Razor 1″-3″

2. Atlantic Razor to 10″

3. Green Razor 2″

RAZOR or JACKKNIFE CLAMS are widespread in sand bars and in shallow sand banks between tide marks. Four groups (genera) of Razor Clams have been classified, but all are generally similar. Razor Clams are prized for their flavor and are dug locally and even commercially. They live in a vertical position in the sand and feed with part of the shell sticking out. The Razor Clams are well represented on the Pacific.

4. Stout Tagelus 2″-3.5″

SURF CLAMS include several related groups, all preferring a surf environment on sandy shores. These clams burrow a few inches into the sand, feeding on minute plant and animal life washed back and forth by the waves. The Atlantic Surf Clam, with a coarse white shell, grows up to 7 in. long. It is often gathered for food. After severe storms, beaches are sometimes covered with millions of

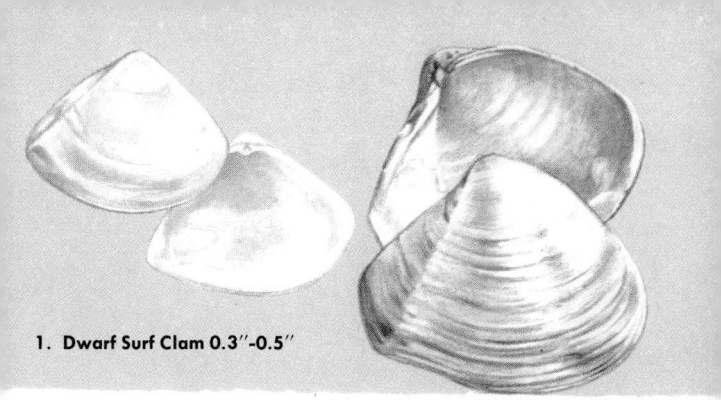

1. Dwarf Surf Clam 0.3″-0.5″

2. Smooth Duck Clam 2″-3″

these clams. Two species are found along the Atlantic shores; five species occur along the Pacific. The Dwarf Surf Clam, usually ½ in. long or less, is very common in warm, shallow waters of the Atlantic and Gulf. The Fragile Atlantic Mactra and California Mactra are species with both ends of the shell rounded. Only the eastern form has a fragile shell. The Duck Clams are similar eastern clams with thin shells. They show a greater preference for mud than do the Mactras.

3. Channeled Duck Clam 2″-3″

SOFT-SHELL CLAMS prefer shallow, muddy bottoms. At low tide, clam diggers locate them as they squirt. Known also as Steamer Clams and Long Clams, they are edible, tasty, and popular. The shell is dull chalky white, with unequal valves that do not close completely. Maximum size is about 6 in. Abundant along the Atlantic Coast, they have been introduced into the San Francisco Bay region.

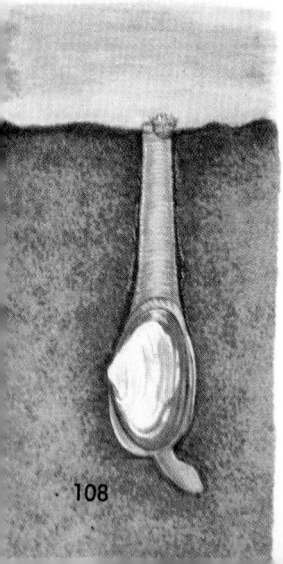

1. Truncate Soft-shell Clam 1″-3″

2. Soft-shell Clam 1″-6″

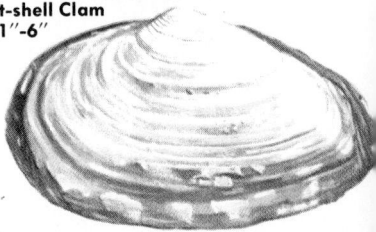

1. Angel Wing
4″-8″

ANGEL WINGS and similar bivalves are species that burrow in mud, clay, or peat, and cannot be collected without hard, careful digging. The Angel Wing lives about a foot below the surface. These species live along the Atlantic, generally preferring warmer water. A number of similar but less attractive species live along the Pacific. Shells of all are thin, somewhat fragile, and often pinkish.

2. False Angel Wing 2″

3. Fallen Angel Wing 2″-2.5″

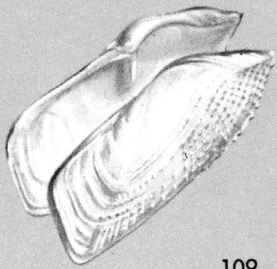

SHIPWORMS (Teredo) are not worms at all but are one of the few destructive bivalves. These animals, with a greatly reduced shell, enter wood as larvae. They remain and grow, digging a circular, twisting burrow with the edge of their shells through piling. Before the days of steel ships, hulls were sheathed with copper to keep out Shipworms. Chemicals deter them, but control is still a major problem. Over 12 species are known. Specimens of bored wood may be found on nearly every beach.

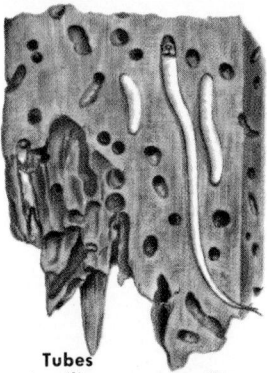

Tubes in piling

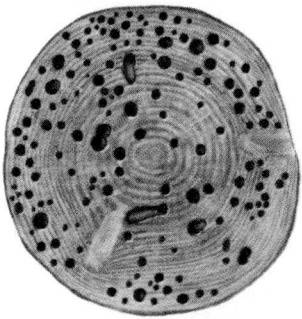

Damage to piling

Common Shipworm

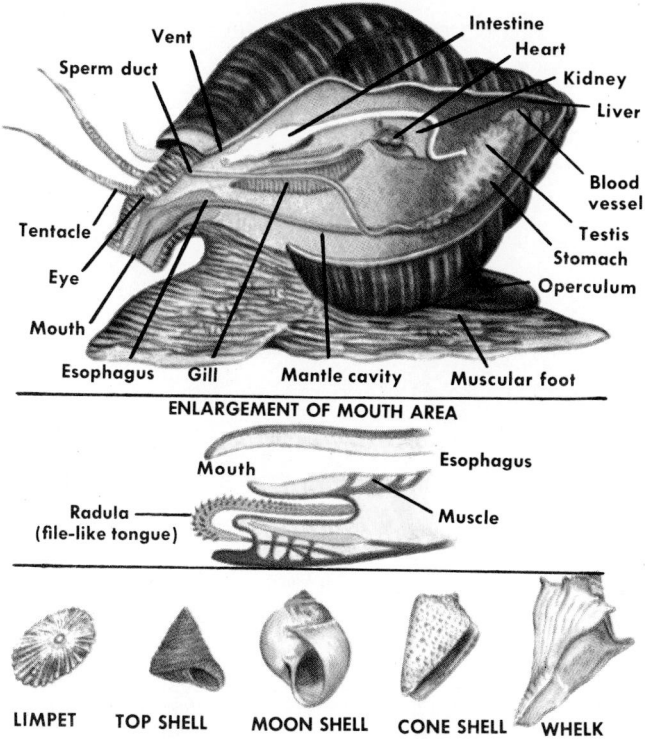

GASTROPODS, often called Sea Snails, are the second large group of mollusks. It includes many fresh-water and land species; the latter are most common in the tropics. Though a few Gastropods have no shell at all, most have a single spiral shell. The animal has a distinct head with eyes and feelers (tentacles). Internal body structures shown above are modified to fit the spiral pattern, evident even in the young, free-swimming larvae. A horny cover or operculum, covering the shell opening, protects the animal when it withdraws.

1. Great Keyhole Limpet 2.5″-4″

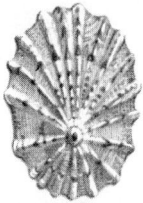

2. Rough Limpet 1.3″

3. Antillean Limpet 0.8″-1″

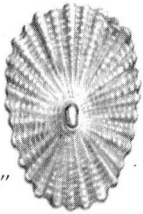

4. Lister's Keyhole Limpet 1″-2″

LIMPETS have spiral shells as larvae but soon settle down and grow their flattened conical shells. A number of species have a hole at the peak of the spiral; others do not. Most Limpets prefer cooler waters of the Atlantic and Pacific. Most grow attached to rocks and may be collected at low tides. Some prefer deeper water, and a few live on larger algae. The Great Keyhole Limpet of the Pacific is our largest species, up to 4 in. long. Animal's mantle covers most of shell.

5. Atlantic Plate Limpet 1″-1.5″

TOP SHELLS and those on the next page point out the wide confusion in common names. Over 50 American species are called Top Shells, including those illustrated. These shells vary from ½ to 4 in. high. Some have a thick, heavy operculum which covers the animal when inside the shell. Larger species are gathered for food, especially on the Asian side of the Pacific. Found in shallow to moderately deep water.

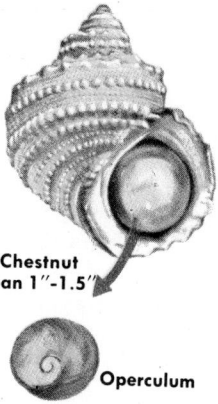

1. Chestnut Turban 1″-1.5″

Operculum

2. Ribbed Top Shell 0.8″-1″

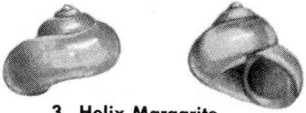

3. Helix Margarite 0.5″

4. Tampa Top Shell 0.5″-1.3″

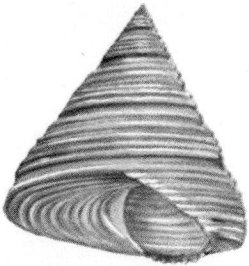

5. Channeled Top Shell 1″-1.5″

TEGULA SHELLS, formerly known as Turban Shells because of their shape, are plant-eating snails of warmer waters. Nearly a dozen species live along the Pacific, but only two occur in shallow waters of southern Florida. West Indies species are more common. All have smooth, iridescent shells; there is a thin, horny, sheet-like covering on the shells of living animals. Most Tegula are from 1 to 2 in. high (Atlantic species, a bit smaller). The Black Tegula is abundant on Pacific shores between the tide marks. The top of the shell is usually worn, disclosing the pearly layer beneath the dark skin.

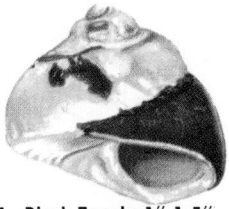

1. Black Tegula 1″-1.5″ (3 views)

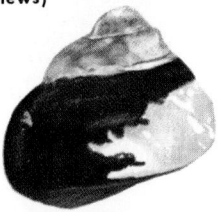

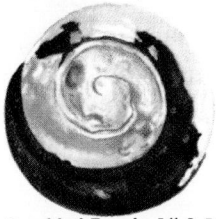

2. Speckled Tegula 1″-1.5″

3. Smooth Atlantic Tegula 0.5″-0.8″ (2 views)

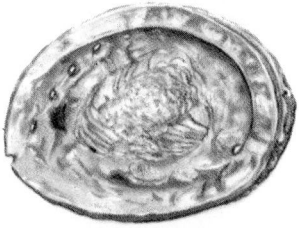

1. Red Abalone 10″-12″

2. Japanese Abalone 4″-6″

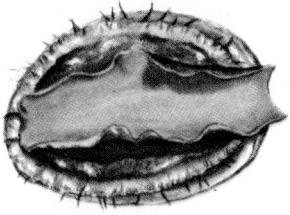

Live Red Abalone

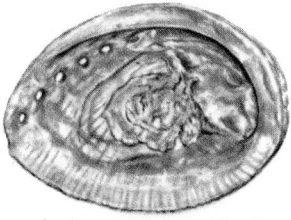

3. Green Abalone 7″-8″

ABALONES, largest and most attractive Pacific Coast shells (4 to 12 in. across), are most common in warmer parts of the Pacific. The shells, prized by Indians and traded far inland, are still used in attractive jewelry. The large muscle is edible and tasty. Abalones caught and canned in lower California are regularly shipped to the Orient. On our coasts they are protected by conservation laws.

4. Black Abalone 6″

1. Brown-banded Wentletrap 0.5″-1″

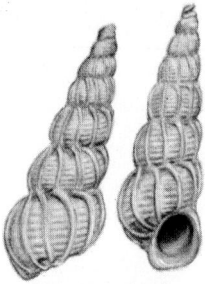

2. Greenland Wentletrap 1″

WENTLETRAPS are Staircase or Ladder Shells. The first name, Wentletrap, is Dutch; it is applied to old spiral staircases. Delicate, symmetrical, and attractive—rare forms of these shells bring high prices from collectors. The animals are carnivorous and live in deep water. They are an important food of larger fish. The shell is a tight, high-spiraled whorl with as many as ten spirals (½ to 1½ in. high). The lip of the shell thickens, forming an isolated ridge during the next growth period.

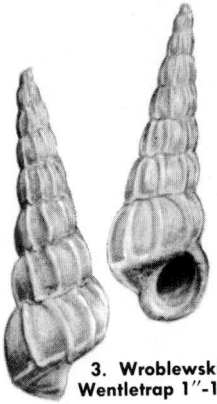

3. Wroblewski's Wentletrap 1″-1.3″

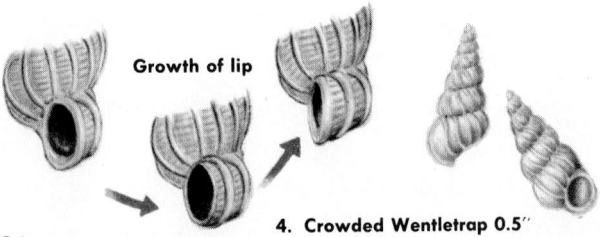

4. Crowded Wentletrap 0.5″

MOON SHELLS and the closely related Natica include about a dozen widely distributed species. Their shells are found on all Atlantic and Pacific beaches. These carnivores feed on other shellfish, which they engulf and smother with the aid of an unusually large foot. Moon Shells build a circular "sand collar," cementing the sand grains with a glue they produce. Eggs are deposited inside this protective ring.

1. Arctic Natica 1″-1.3″

2. Colorful Atlantic Natica 1″-2″

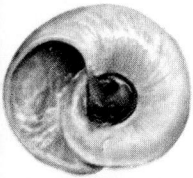

3. Shark Eye 1″-2.5″

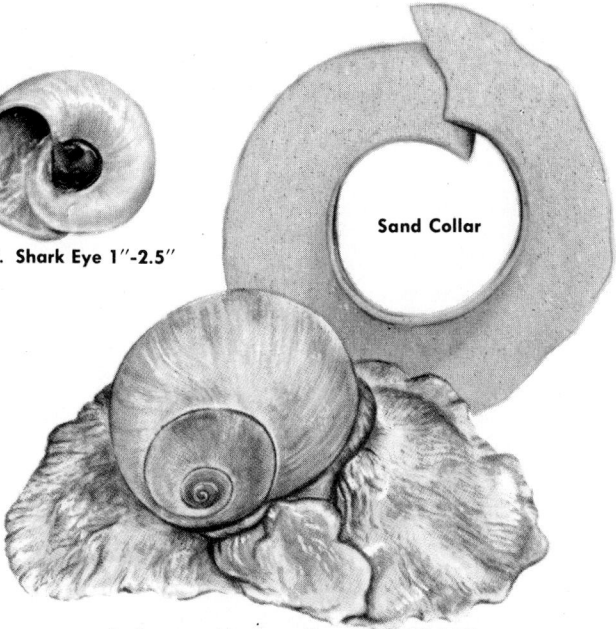

4. Common Northern Moon Shell 2″-4.5″

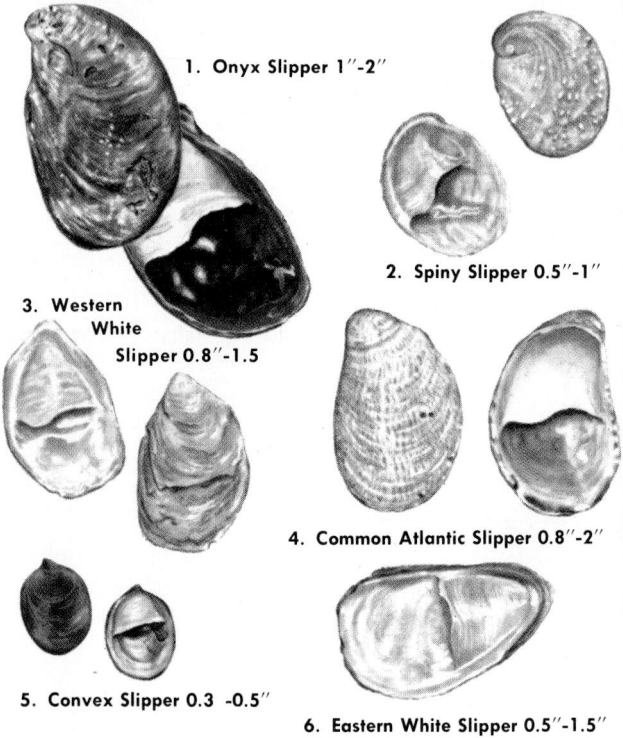

SLIPPER or BOAT SHELLS are odd animals ¼ to 2 in. long. They lead a fixed existence somewhat like that of Limpets. All the shells have, internally, a small horizontal platform or deck somewhat like that of an old sailing ship. This and the shape of the shell give these species their name. Collectors find these common shells washed up on every beach. The animals live in shallow water attached to rocks or other shells. Slippers occur in all the temperate and tropical seas. There are about nine American species.

PERIWINKLES are probably better known than any other mollusks. The common species has come from Europe, where it is a favored sea food. During the past century it has spread rapidly along the Atlantic Coast. They are seldom eaten in this country. About 12 species of Periwinkle are equally distributed on rocky beaches of both our coasts. Length is ½ to slightly over 1 in. All are drab-colored, though some are spotted or mottled. Periwinkles feed on algae.

1. Checkered Periwinkle 0.5″

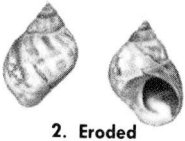

2. Eroded Periwinkle 0.5″-0.8″

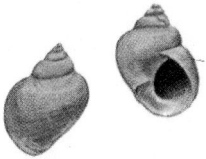

3. Northern Rough Periwinkle 0.3″-0.5″

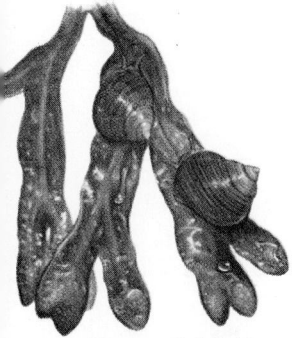

Common Periwinkles on seaweed

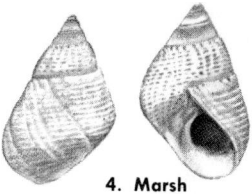

4. Marsh Periwinkle 1″

5. Common Periwinkle 0.8″-1″

6. Angulate Periwinkle 1″

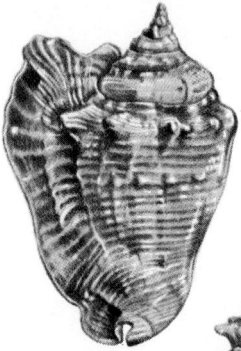

1. Hawk-wing Conch 2″-4″

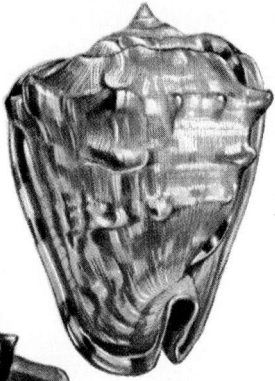

2. King Helmet 4″-9″

3. Florida Fighting Conch 3″-4″

CONCH and HELMET SHELLS are found on sandy bottoms of shallow tropical waters. Species of these widespread groups occur from the Carolinas south. Shells are often for sale in stores and roadside stands. All are large (2 to 12 in. long). Helmet Shells are carnivorous. Conchs feed on algae. The Queen Conch, one of the largest gastropods, is commonly eaten in the form of chowder. The heavy, triangular, thick-lipped Helmet Shells are used in making cameos. The thick shell and variable colors suit them especially well for this purpose.

Living Queen Conch

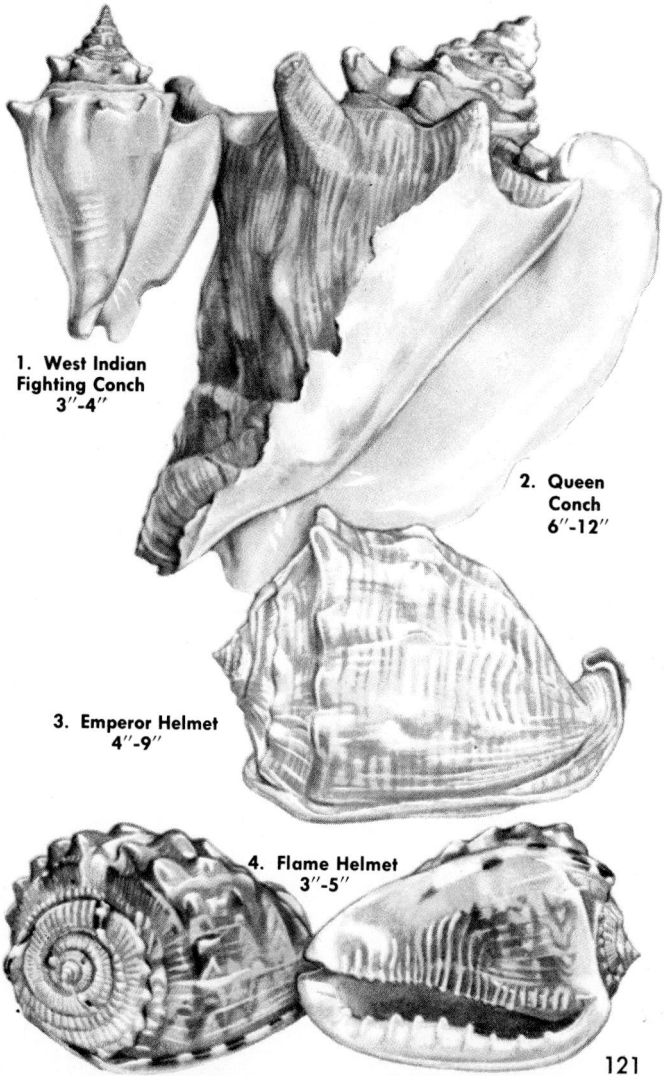
1. West Indian
Fighting Conch
3″-4″
2. Queen
Conch
6″-12″
3. Emperor Helmet
4″-9″
4. Flame Helmet
3″-5″

HORNSHELLS and their kin are small (¼ to 1½ in. long) animals common on mud, seaweeds, and in tide pools along both coasts. Most prefer shallow water and are common in the tidal zone. All feed on sea plants, especially on eelgrass. Several groups, totaling about 100 species, are embraced by the common name. Atlantic species are more common on Florida and other southern beaches. Some Pacific species prefer colder water. All these animals have sharply spired shells with from 10 to 15 or more spirals.

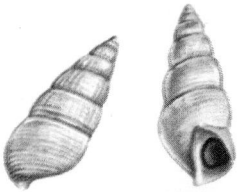

1. Alternate Bittium 0.2″-0.3″

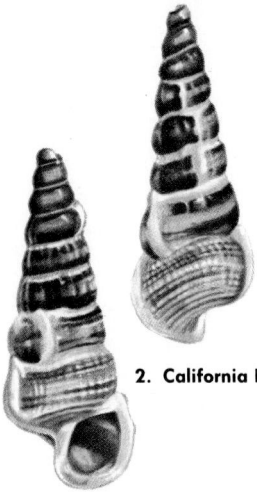

2. California Hornshell 1″-1.3″

4. Florida Cerith 1″-1.5″

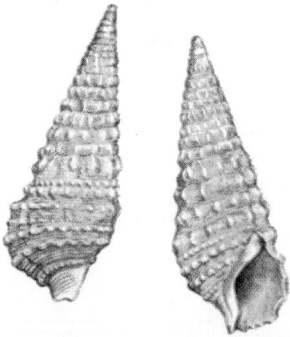

3. False Cerith 0.5″-0.8″

1. Giant Tun 5″-7″

2. Partridge Tun 2″-5″

TUN or CASK SHELLS are large, thin-walled, rounded shells, mostly tropical. A few species occur on our southern Atlantic Coast—none off California. These shells are 2 to 10 in. long. The moving animal is much larger and, like some other gastropods, seems too big for its shell. Members of this family prefer deeper water. Fig Shell, shown here with the live animal protruding from its shell, is a close relative.

3. Common Fig Shell 3″-4″

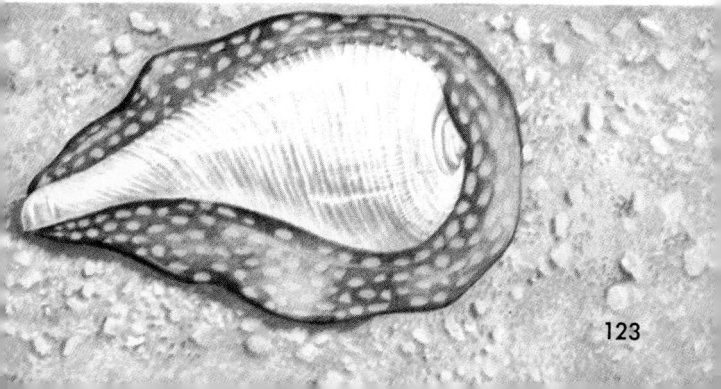

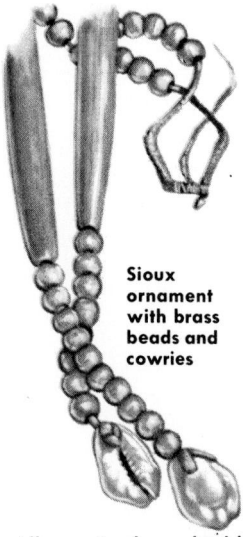

Sioux ornament with brass beads and cowries

COWRIES are perhaps better known than any other group of mollusks. People the world over have been attracted by their beauty. Smaller kinds have been made into ornaments, and a yellow species was long traded and used as money in Africa and other regions. The spiral shell of cowries can be seen only in young animals. As the animal grows, the lime deposited in the large body spiral gradually engulfs the remaining twists of the shell. In mature cowries, all trace of the spiral shell is lost. All cowries have highly polished shells; a few are plain, but many are mottled and brightly colored. All are tropical species, and only a limited number occur in our warmer waters—one on the Pacific Coast and about a dozen on the Atlantic. Most cowries are from 1 to 4 in. long. The Coffee Bean Shells, smaller relatives of cowries, are all less than 1 in. A closely related group is found along the Pacific. Most cowries prefer moderately deep water.

Live Chestnut Cowry

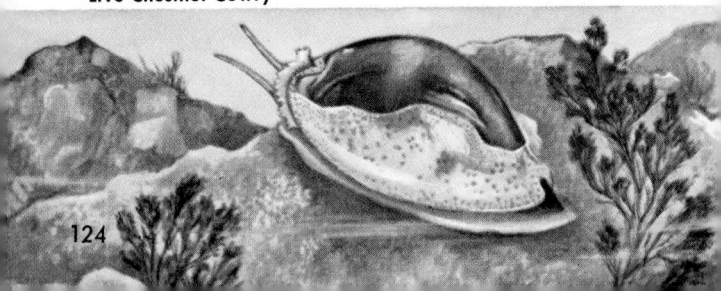

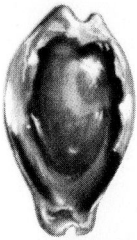

1. Chestnut Cowry
1″-2″

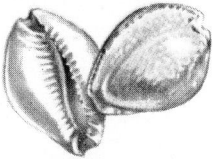

2. Atlantic Yellow Cowry
0.5″-1.3″

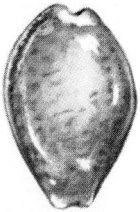

3. Atlantic
Gray Cowry
0.8″-1.5″

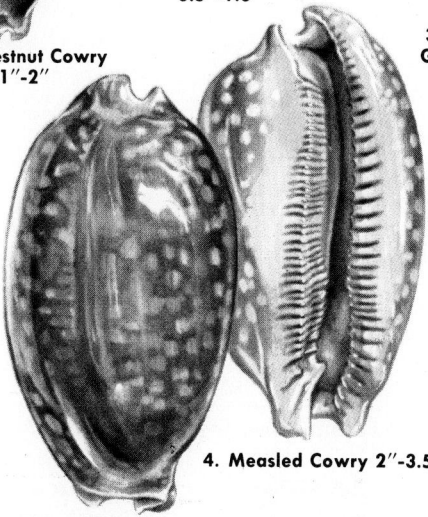

4. Measled Cowry 2″-3.5″

5. Solander's Coffee
Bean 0.8″

6. California
Coffee Bean 0.3″-0.5″

7. Four-spotted
Coffee Bean
0.1″-0.3″

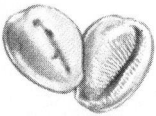

8. Atlantic
Coffee
Bean 0.5″

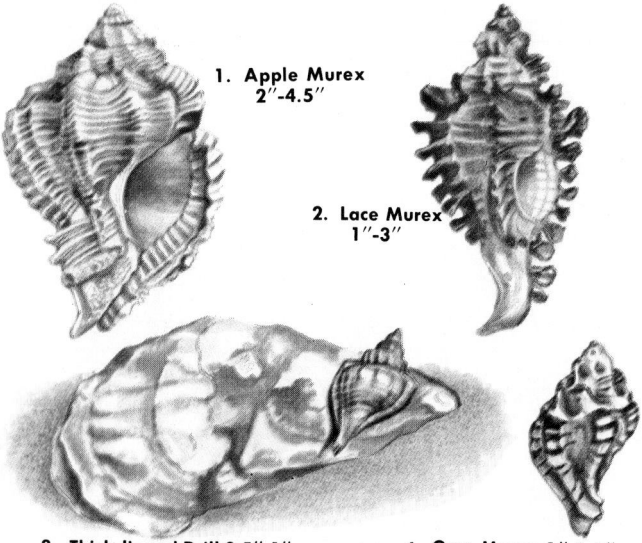

MUREX SHELLS and their kin include over a thousand species, counting the Drills (p. 128), which have become serious pests in oyster beds. All of this group are carnivores, feeding mainly on bivalves. Shells are about 1 in. to 6 in. high; heavy, ridged, and usually spiny. Most showy species are tropical, though some are also found in temperate waters. Typical and best known is the Murex group, a widespread genus, found on our south Atlantio and Gulf coasts, and farther south. The West Indian Murex, large (6 in.) and showy, is a rare species. Fewer kinds, and a number of related species, live on our Pacific shores. Murex snails live in moderately deep water. Shells are often washed up on beaches. The Drills and other shallow-water species can be collected at low tides.

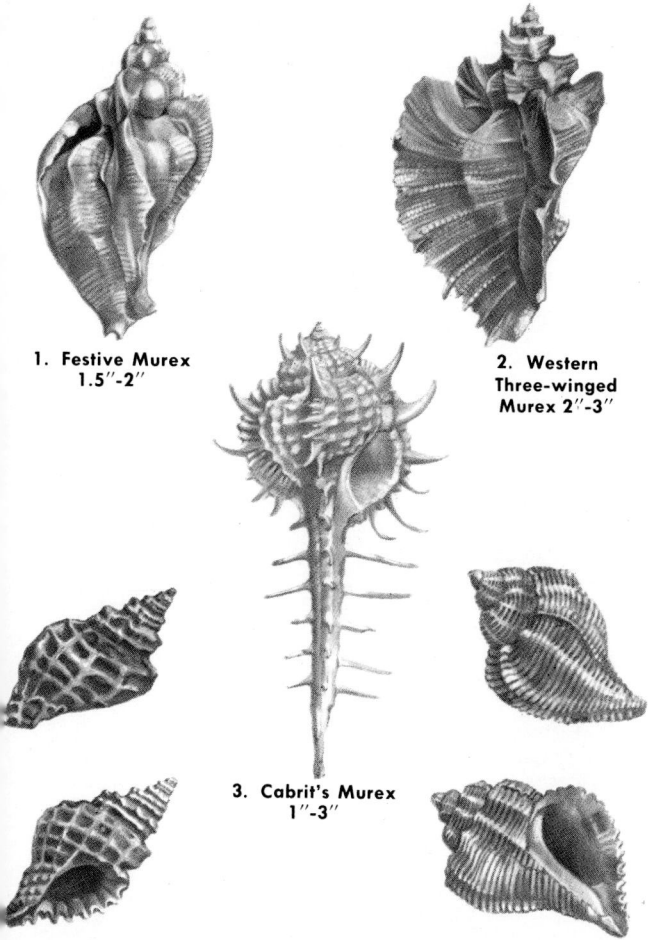

1. Festive Murex
1.5″-2″

2. Western
Three-winged
Murex 2″-3″

3. Cabrit's Murex
1″-3″

4. Carpenter's Dwarf Triton
0.5″-0.8″

5. Circled Dwarf Triton
0.8″-1″

OYSTER DRILLS, DOGWINKLES and PURPURAS are related to Murex. These smaller species (½ to 3½ in. long) look like miniature, less showy forms. Oyster Drills use a tongue-like file to drill a hole through bivalve shells and use a sucking tube to eat the animal within. Animals of this group (and some other species of Murex, too) were crushed to obtain the famous royal purple dye used by Greeks and Romans. These animals are common on rocks and in tide pools on both our coasts, and in shallow temperate waters around the world.

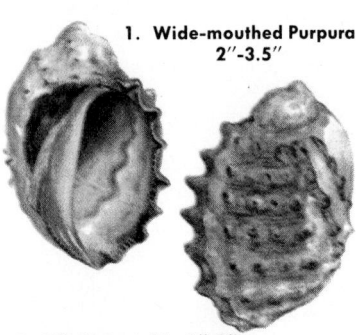

1. Wide-mouthed Purpura 2″-3.5″

2. Atlantic Oyster Drill 0.5″-1″

3. File Dogwinkle 1″-2″

4. Emarginate Dogwinkle 1″

Oyster Drill on oyster

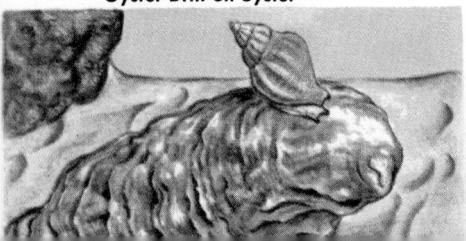

5. Atlantic Dogwinkle 1″-2″

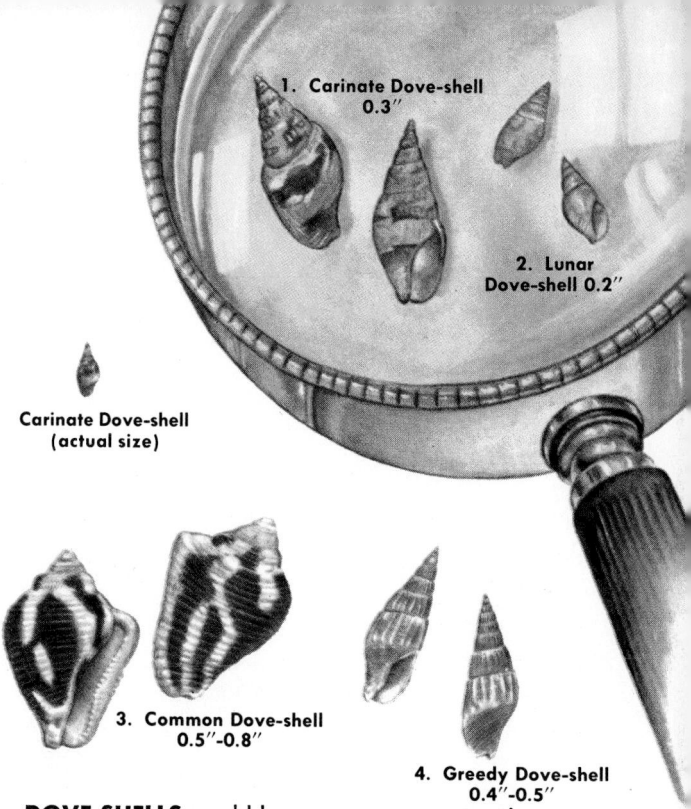

DOVE-SHELLS would be an even more attractive group of shells if only they were larger. American species are well under an inch long—some less than ¼ in. These small animals are common and can be collected as they crawl over rocks and seaweeds at low tide. The spindle-shaped shells have a thickening at the center of the lip. They are shiny and often brightly marked. More varieties of Dove-shells live on the East Coast than on the West. They occur along the full length of each coast, but are more common in warmer waters.

1. Channeled Whelk 5″-7.5″

2. Knobbed Whelk 5″-9″

Egg cases of Knobbed Whelk

3. Tabled Neptune 3″-4″

4. Ten-ridged Whelk 3″-4.5″

WHELKS are the largest northern gastropods, 3 to 16 in. long. While not so attractive as some southern forms, they have little competition on northern beaches. The animals drill bivalve shells with a rasping, tongue-like structure (like the Oyster Drill) and feed on the animal inside. The Knobbed Whelk is the largest, and the Channeled Whelk almost as big. Both occur from Cape Cod south along Atlantic and Gulf shores. In summer, strings of horny egg cases of these whelks are found on the beach—sometimes with hundreds of very tiny

1. Lightning Whelk 4″-16″

2. Pear Whelk 3″-4″

3. Common Northern Buccinum 2″-4″

perfect shells within. The Pear Whelk, more delicately formed, is a southern whelk. Dozens of smaller whelks also occur along northern shores. All are carnivores and scavengers. Some of these are widely used as food in Europe. The Knobbed and Channeled Whelks also are eaten and are sometimes found in markets.

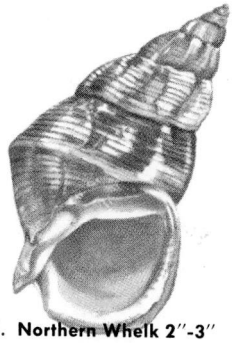

4. Northern Whelk 2″-3″

1. Mud Snail
0.8″-1″

2. Eastern Nassa
0.5″

3. New England Nassa 0.8″

4. Giant Western
Nassa 1.5″-2″

NASSAS and MUD SNAILS are small species, ½ to 1 in. long, and much more common than the larger and better-known whelks. The Mud Snail, sometimes called Basket Shell, is the most common species, especially in the north. Mud Snails may be seen by the thousands when mud flats are exposed at low tide. They are scavengers, but also attack and eat bivalves. Because they are so abundant, these animals are an important factor in shore life. The Nassas, which also favor mud flats, are more common southward.

1. Banded Tulip
2″-4″

TULIP SHELLS or BAND SHELLS are large, thick-shelled carnivorous gastropods of warmer seas. Three species live on our south Atlantic shores. Some smaller related shells, belonging to the same family, are found along the California beaches. Best known of this group is the large Florida Horse Conch (1 to 2 ft.), largest gastropod in American waters. The living animal is even more attractive than its handsomely colored shell.

2. Florida
Horse Conch
1′-2′

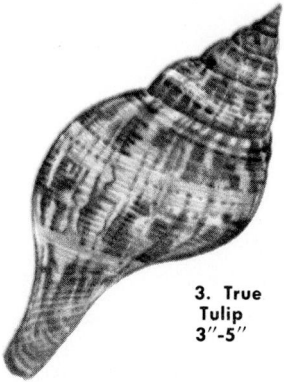

3. True
Tulip
3″-5″

1. Lettered Olive 2″-2.5″

2. Variable Dwarf Olive 0.3″-0.5″

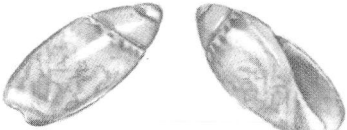

3. Beatic Dwarf Olive 0.5″-0.8″

4. Purple Dwarf Olive 1″-1.3″

OLIVE SHELLS are somewhat similar to Cowries (pp. 124-125) in that the growing shell engulfs much of its spire. Olive Shells are small (½ to 2½ in. long), but the family is a large one, of many tropical species. Our species occur on both the Atlantic and Pacific coasts—some extending into northern waters. The animal is quite large, and when it is completely extended the shell is hidden. The bright gray or bluish shells were prized ornaments of Indians. Olive Shells are common in shallow water and are found on sandy beaches.

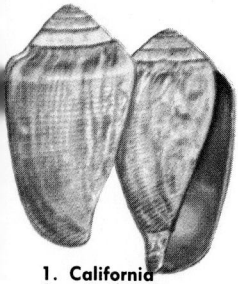

1. California Cone 0.8″-1″

2. Mouse Cone 1″-1.5″

CONE SHELLS are a tropical group. This large family is represented by a single species on our Pacific shores and by about a dozen Atlantic species, mainly from Florida's rocks and corals. More common in the West Indies. Some tropical species are poisonous and can give a fatal sting. But none of these lives in our area. Ours vary from just under 1 in. to about 3 in. long. They are brightly colored in yellows and browns and are best identified by their typical conical shape and attractive markings. Cone shells are collectors' favorites. The Glory-of-the-Seas, most valuable of all shells, is a rare Cone Shell from the East Indies.

3. Crown Cone 2″-3″

4. Florida Cone 1.5″-1.8″

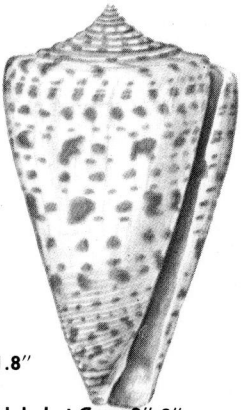

5. Alphabet Cone 2″-3″

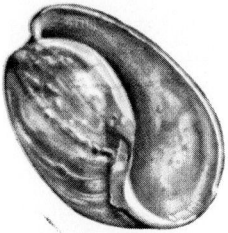

1. California Bubble
1.5″-2″

2. Eastern Paper Bubble
0.5″

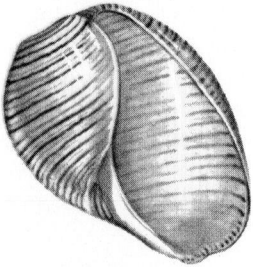

3. Brown-lined
Paper Bubble 1″-1.5″

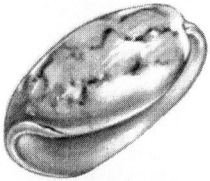

4. West Indian Bubble
0.5″-1″

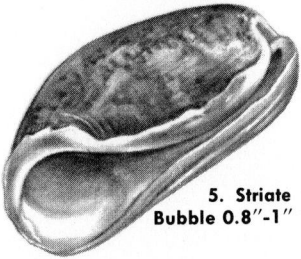

5. Striate
Bubble 0.8″-1″

BUBBLE SHELLS belong to several closely related families, which differ from other gastropods in several ways. The animal has two pairs of tentacles. The shell is smaller than the animal, loosely curved, thin and brittle. Most species live in shallow, warm water. They are closely related to the shell-less Sea Slugs. Nearly all are less than ½ in. long. Those illustrated are among the largest and showiest species.

SEA SLUGS are a paradox—shell-less shellfish. However, some land snails are without shells also. The embryo has a coiled shell, but this is lost soon after the Sea Slug emerges. Sea Slugs vary considerably in size and color. The Plumed Sea Slug, one of the larger American species, grows up to 4 in. long. Others are much smaller. These odd animals feed partly on Sea Anemones and are able to use the stinging cells taken from their prey as part of their own body defenses. Most Sea Slugs are cold-water animals.

SQUID, OCTOPUS, and their kin are mollusks in which the foot is modified into a ring of tentacles, bearing cup-like suction discs around the mouths. Giant Octopus and Giant Squid are rare, deep-water animals. None is as big as the stories told about them. Other species of both animals are common, harmless, and often prized as food.

Squids, common along both our coasts, usually travel in schools. Most species are 8 to 20 in. long, though the Giant Squid measures up to 50 ft. The Squid shell is reduced to a soft internal plate, the "pen." A muscular mantle covers the body. Squids are jet-propelled: they swim by ejecting a stream of water which shoots them backward. Squids encircle small fish with their tentacles and eat with sharp horny beaks set around their mouths. They protect themselves by emitting an inky fluid, and hide from their enemies in this smoke screen.

Pacific Octopus

Octopus prefers shallower water than the Squid and is often found under rocks at low tide. These unusual animals feed mostly on crabs. The Octopus (and also the Squid) can change color rapidly, especially when excited or feeding. The colors are usually browns, yellows, and a dull rose. The Octopus moves along the bottom, using its tentacles, or swims by jet propulsion like Squids. From eggs laid in jellied clusters on rocks, the young emerge as miniature adults. Atlantic and Pacific shore species are similar in appearance.

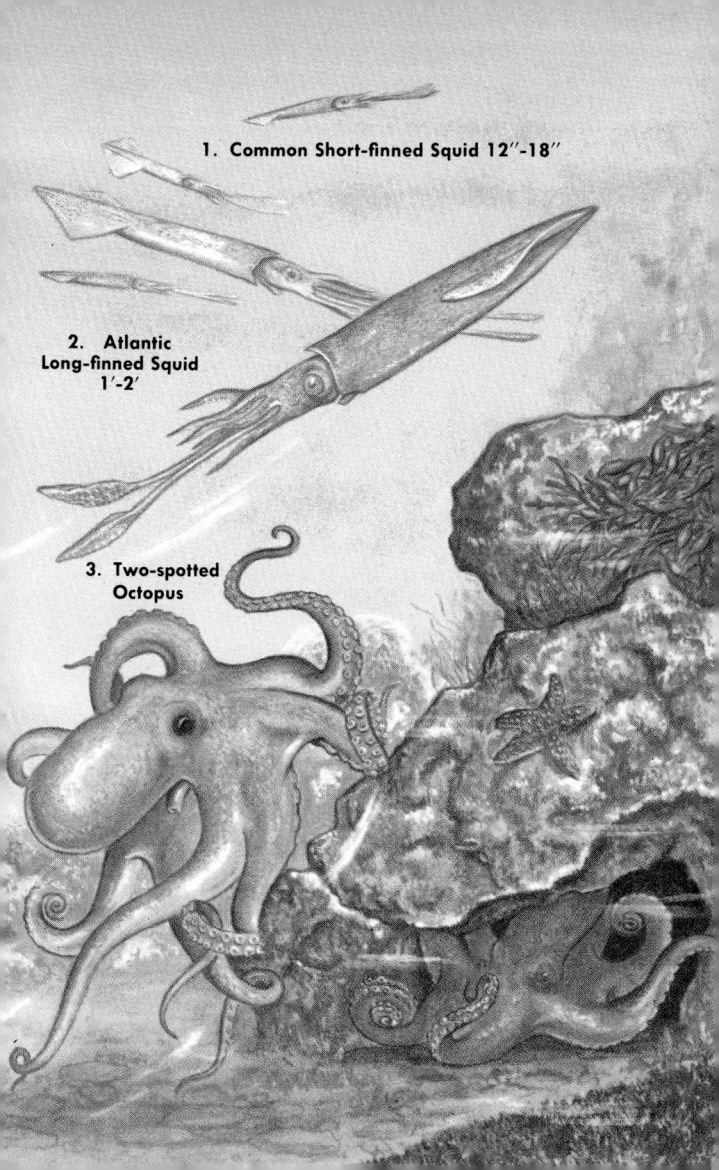
1. Common Short-finned Squid 12″-18″
2. Atlantic Long-finned Squid 1′-2′
3. Two-spotted Octopus

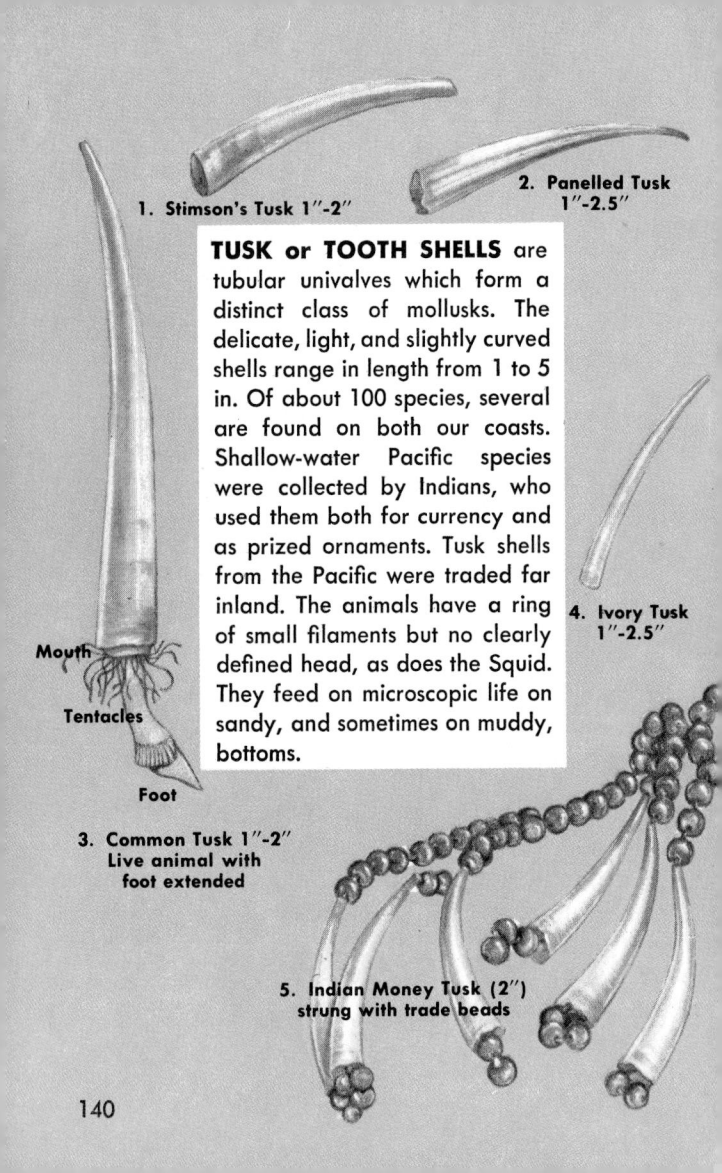

TUSK or TOOTH SHELLS are tubular univalves which form a distinct class of mollusks. The delicate, light, and slightly curved shells range in length from 1 to 5 in. Of about 100 species, several are found on both our coasts. Shallow-water Pacific species were collected by Indians, who used them both for currency and as prized ornaments. Tusk shells from the Pacific were traded far inland. The animals have a ring of small filaments but no clearly defined head, as does the Squid. They feed on microscopic life on sandy, and sometimes on muddy, bottoms.

Beach Plums spot dunes from Massachusetts to Virginia.

PLANTS OF DUNE AND SHORE

In the long run, all animal life of the sea depends upon plants—hence the importance of algae. Seed-producing aquatic species also grow in brackish or salt water. Less important but of special interest are many land plants which have adapted themselves to the seashore environment. Some grow on beach sands or dunes, or in crevices of sea cliffs. Shores resemble deserts in some ways, and shore plants often show characteristics of plants in arid regions. Some have deep, penetrating roots and small leathery, hairy, or waxy leaves. A number are succulents capable of storing water. All are thrifty and resistant to wind, salt spray, and drought.

Of the plants along the shore, members of the grass and sedge families have been most successful. These are often less conspicuous and more difficult to identify. Other flowering plants range from small herbaceous species to shrubs and trees. The latter include, besides those illustrated, pines, cedar, hollies, sumac, and others. The herbaceous plants are more numerous and so diverse that only a few are shown on the following pages. Also read:

AQUATIC PLANTS OF THE UNITED STATES, Muenscher, Cornell Univ. Press (Comstock), Ithaca, New York, 1944.
FLOWERS, Zim and Martin, Golden Press, New York, 1950.
TREES, Zim and Martin, Golden Press, New York, 1952.

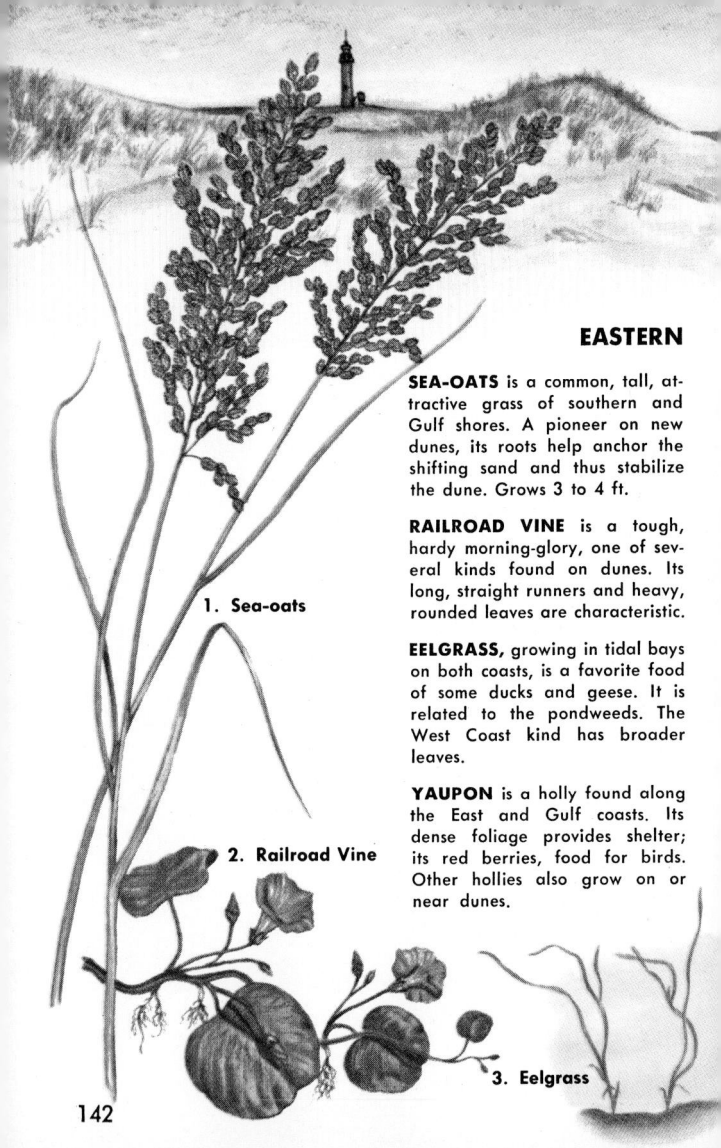

EASTERN

SEA-OATS is a common, tall, attractive grass of southern and Gulf shores. A pioneer on new dunes, its roots help anchor the shifting sand and thus stabilize the dune. Grows 3 to 4 ft.

RAILROAD VINE is a tough, hardy morning-glory, one of several kinds found on dunes. Its long, straight runners and heavy, rounded leaves are characteristic.

EELGRASS, growing in tidal bays on both coasts, is a favorite food of some ducks and geese. It is related to the pondweeds. The West Coast kind has broader leaves.

YAUPON is a holly found along the East and Gulf coasts. Its dense foliage provides shelter; its red berries, food for birds. Other hollies also grow on or near dunes.

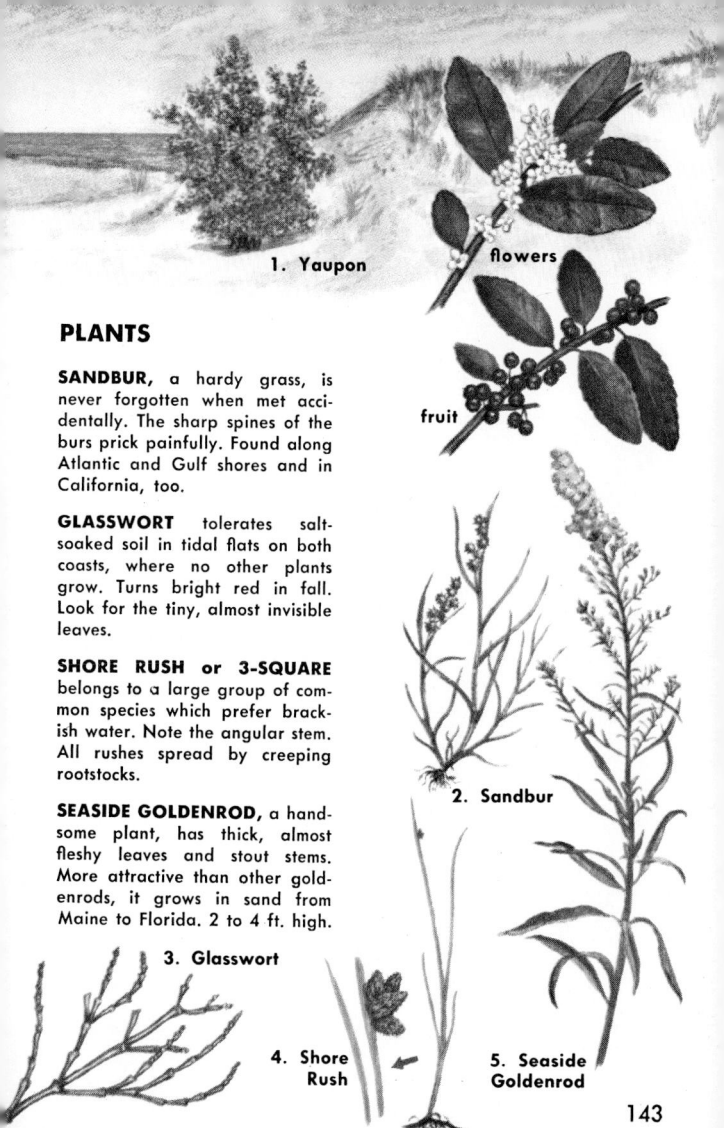

1. Yaupon

PLANTS

SANDBUR, a hardy grass, is never forgotten when met accidentally. The sharp spines of the burs prick painfully. Found along Atlantic and Gulf shores and in California, too.

GLASSWORT tolerates salt-soaked soil in tidal flats on both coasts, where no other plants grow. Turns bright red in fall. Look for the tiny, almost invisible leaves.

SHORE RUSH or 3-SQUARE belongs to a large group of common species which prefer brackish water. Note the angular stem. All rushes spread by creeping rootstocks.

SEASIDE GOLDENROD, a handsome plant, has thick, almost fleshy leaves and stout stems. More attractive than other goldenrods, it grows in sand from Maine to Florida. 2 to 4 ft. high.

2. Sandbur

3. Glasswort

4. Shore Rush

5. Seaside Goldenrod

WESTERN

LUPINES vary from small herbs to large shrubs. Several kinds, with spikes of blue or yellow flowers, grow along western beaches. Tree lupine is the largest of these species.

SEA-FIG and related ice plants are unusual, thick-leaved plants found along shores in many warmer countries. Sea-fig is prolific, thrifty, and attractive. Its fruit is edible.

BEACH PEAS include several species. Some are hairy; some smooth and thin-leaved. Flowers usually purple; seeds in a thin pod. Related to sweet and garden peas.

SAND STRAWBERRY is a small, short-stemmed plant on or near the beaches and on open prairies. Blooms and fruits early in spring. Fruit delicious but small.

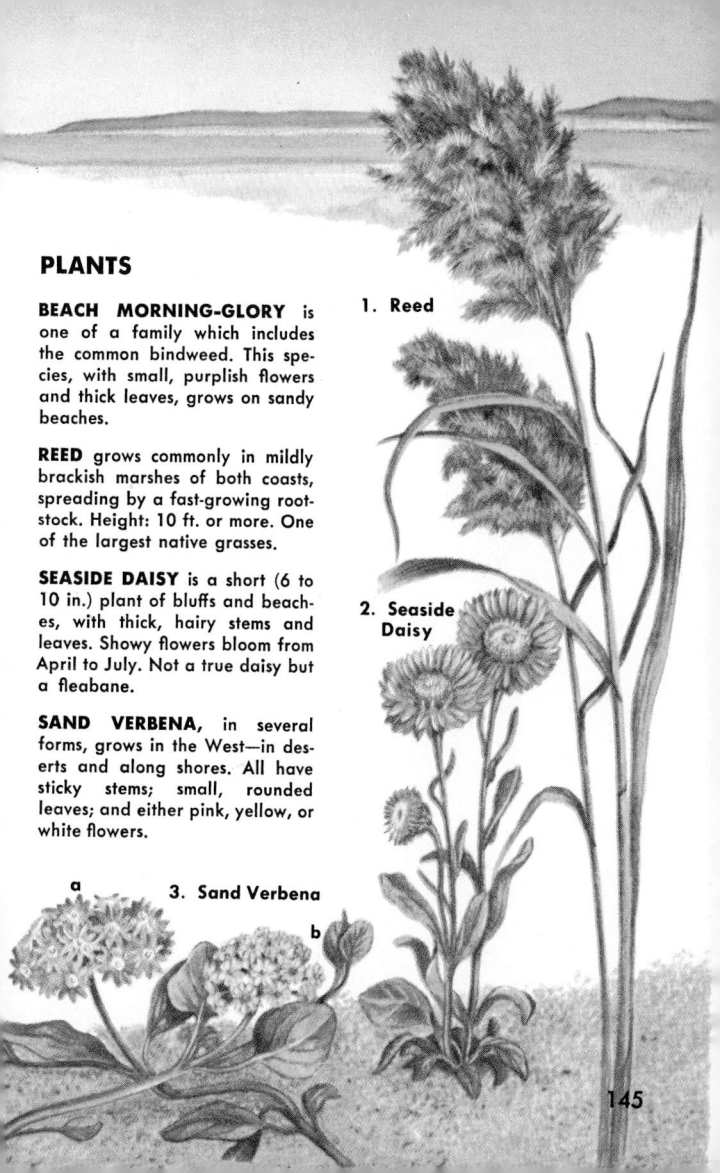

PLANTS

BEACH MORNING-GLORY is one of a family which includes the common bindweed. This species, with small, purplish flowers and thick leaves, grows on sandy beaches.

REED grows commonly in mildly brackish marshes of both coasts, spreading by a fast-growing rootstock. Height: 10 ft. or more. One of the largest native grasses.

SEASIDE DAISY is a short (6 to 10 in.) plant of bluffs and beaches, with thick, hairy stems and leaves. Showy flowers bloom from April to July. Not a true daisy but a fleabane.

SAND VERBENA, in several forms, grows in the West—in deserts and along shores. All have sticky stems; small, rounded leaves; and either pink, yellow, or white flowers.

1. Saw Palmetto

2. Cabbage Palmetto

SHORE TREES

PALMETTOS are southern trees. Some cover mile after mile of sandy soil behind the beaches. Usually shrubby, some grow 20 to 30 ft. high, topped by large clusters of fan-shaped leaves.

BAYBERRY or WAX MYRTLE, common along dunes and beaches, produces wax-covered "berries," once used for candles and still as a food by many birds. Does not get as close to salt water as Mangrove.

SEA-GRAPE is one of the most attractive shore trees of the deep South. It grows on dunes or coral. The large, leathery leaves are tinged red; the small purple fruit gives it its name.

MANGROVE is unmistakable. Its spreading prop-roots and tolerance of salt water make it the most common plant for long stretches of Florida and Gulf coasts. Watch for awl-shaped seedlings on beaches.

3. Bayberry

4. Sea-grape

5. Mangrove

Brown Pelican

BIRDS of sea and shore add a sparkle of life whenever they appear. Some venture far out to sea. Others live and move along the shore, which is one of the best places to study birds, especially while migrating. The birds in this book supplement those in BIRDS, a Golden Nature Guide.

Birds of the shore include sandpipers, terns, pelicans, herons, gulls, ducks, and others adapted to life on water or along the shore. Many land birds live along the shores also. Seaside and Sharptailed Sparrows, Boat-tailed Grackles, Tree Swallows, and larks are found in or near salt swamps. Ospreys, eagles, crows, and Fish-crows prefer open headlands or more protected bays and lagoons. In spring and fall, many migrating land birds follow the shoreline. Some shore birds, too, migrate. Do more than identify birds; watch them feed and fly. See a whole flock maneuver together with unerring accuracy. Illustrations show adult birds in spring plumage. Further reading:

BIRDS, Zim and Gabrielson, Golden Press, New York, 1955.

A FIELD GUIDE TO THE BIRDS and A FIELD GUIDE TO WESTERN BIRDS, Peterson, Houghton Mifflin Co., Boston, 1947, 1941.

BIRDS OF THE PACIFIC STATES, Hoffman, R., Houghton Mifflin Co., Boston, 1938.

OYSTERCATCHERS are waders of rocky shores of both coasts. These stocky birds, 16 to 18 in., with black heads and heavy red bills are quickly recognized. In flight the eastern species shows white wing patches. The Western Black Oystercatcher has no white.

SEMIPALMATED PLOVER, a rather small (6 to 8 in.) bird with a black collar and a short bill. Often it is seen running along the sand or flying low over surf. Note its short tail and dark brown back.

RUDDY TURNSTONE (8 to 9½ in.) migrates down both coasts along both sandy and rocky shores. Look for the white head and rusty brown back. In flight note the striking brown-and-white wing pattern.

DOWITCHER is a snipe-like bird (10½ to 12 in.) with a long, straight bill. On mudflats, sandy beaches and salt marshes it continually probes the mud for food. Note its rusty color, whitish back and rump.

WILLETS are large (14 to 17 in.), fairly drab birds with long, straight bills and long, dark legs. Seen along both coasts, in marshes and mudflats. In flight, the black-and-white wing pattern identifies them.

AVOCETS (17 to 20 in.) are marked by their long, thin, upturned bills, and by their longer, thin black legs. Note the pale brown head and neck, and the strongly marked black-and-white wings. More common on the West Coast in quiet lagoons and mud flats.

KNOTS are cinnamon-brown in spring; gray and white in winter. They are smaller (10-11 in.) than Dowitchers and have shorter bills. Common during spring and fall migrations.

SANDERLING (7 to 8 in.), common in winter on both coasts, is a stocky sandpiper showing a broad white stripe on the wings. Feeds on small invertebrates along surf or in mud flats.

PECTORAL SANDPIPERS migrate along both coasts and are partial to coastal swamps. Note the white throat and abdomen, crossed by a broad, streaked band. Legs thin and yellow; length: 8½ to 9½ in.

SEMIPALMATED SANDPIPER and the almost identical Western Sandpiper of the Pacific are very common during migrations. Streaked dark brown above with dark legs and short, dark bill. Length: 5½ to 6½ in.

1. Herring Gull 2. Laughing Gull

GULLS are common on all shores and along many lakes and rivers. Most common in the East is the Herring Gull (22 to 26 in.), marked by black wing tips and pinkish legs. Several other gulls are similar. The California Gull of the West Coast (20 to 23 in.) is slightly smaller, with dark legs and with a red spot near the tip of its lower bill. The Ring-billed Gull also is similar but smaller (18 to 19 in.), with a black ring around its yellowish bill and with dull yellow legs. The Western Gull is like the California Gull, but has a yellow bill with a red spot, and flesh-colored legs. The Laughing Gull is 15 to 17 in. It is black-headed in spring, and with very dark wings and back. The Great Black-backed Gull is a northern bird seen mainly in winter along Atlantic shores. Its large size (28 to 31 in.) and dark back identify it. The Black Skimmer of the East Coast is a striking bird with black back and wings, and white below. It uses its red underslung bill to scoop up small fish.

3. Ring-billed Gull 4. Western Gull 5. California Gull

1. Royal Tern 2. Common Tern

TERNS The Royal Tern is a handsome bird of southern shores—Atlantic and Pacific. Note its black, crested crown, the orange bill, and the deeply forked tail. Length: 19 to 21 in. The Caspian Tern is similar in range, size, and general appearance. It has a red bill, and tail is less forked. The Common Tern is easy to see and identify. Note its black cap, forked tail, and black-tipped orange bill. Length: 13 to 16 in. Forster's Tern, more common in the West, generally lighter, prefers marshes to open sandy beaches. The Arctic Tern is grayer, with bill completely red.

3. Arctic Tern 4. Forster's Tern 6. Great Black-backed Gull

5. Black Skimmer

WOOD STORK 34 to 38 in. Large flocks along southern shores. Note black on wings, gray head. Flies with neck out.

DOUBLE - CRESTED CORMORANT Ranges farther north than others on this page. Often suns with wings out. Large (28 to 34 in.).

WHITE IBIS Smaller (22 to 26 in.), almost all white. Red face. Seen in large flocks over coastal swamps.

WATER TURKEY or ANHINGA Prefers marshes, lagoons, coastal rivers. Glossy, greenish-gray back, with light wing patches.

GREAT BLUE HERON 40 to 50 in. Common both coasts. White Heron of Florida: larger, pure white, yellow bill and legs.

REDDISH EGRET 28 to 32 in.; on warmer coasts of both oceans. A white phase is similar to Common Egret.

LITTLE BLUE HERONS 20 to 25 in. Young: white or blue-blotched. Green Heron smaller; yellow legs, white on throat. Both coasts.

COMMON EGRET 34 to 40 in. Common on both coasts. Snowy Egret is 8 to 24 in., has yellow feet, black bill and legs.

BOOKS FOR FURTHER STUDY Systematic and exact identification is often difficult. You may need the aid of technical publications, such as journals of scientific societies and museums. Less technical books include:

Abbott, R. T., AMERICAN SEASHELLS, D. Van Nostrand Co., 1954. A major reference. Over 1,500 varieties. Excellent bibliography.

Buchsbaum, R., ANIMALS WITHOUT BACKBONES, Univ. of Chicago Press, 1948. Readable, college-level introduction. Excellent illustrations.

Carson, Rachel, THE EDGE OF THE SEA, New American Library, N. Y., 1955. A very readable introduction to the many living things at the sea's edge.

MacGinitie, G. E. and N., NATURAL HISTORY OF MARINE ANIMALS, McGraw-Hill Book Co., 1949. A fairly detailed, usable summary.

Miner, R. W., FIELD BOOK OF SEASHORE LIFE, G. P. Putnam's Sons, 1950. A very complete and authentic guide for the Atlantic Coast.

Ricketts, E. F. & C. J., BETWEEN PACIFIC TIDES, Stanford Univ. Press, 1952. All tide-zone Pacific invertebrates. Readable; fine photos.

MUSEUMS, AQUARIA, AND MARINE BIOLOGICAL STATIONS of interest to serious amateurs include:

American Museum of Natural History, New York, N. Y.
Chicago Museum of Natural History, Chicago, Ill.
Shedd Aquarium, Chicago, Ill.
Marine Biological Laboratory, Woods Hole, Mass.
Duke Univ. Marine Laboratory, Beaufort, N. C.
Institute of Marine Science, University of Miami, Virginia Key, Miami, Fla.
Oceanographic Institute of Florida State Univ., Alligator Harbor, Fla.
Gulf Coast Research Laboratory, Ocean Springs, Miss.
Hopkins Marine Station, Pacific Grove, Calif.
Puget Sound Marine Biol. Station, Univ. of Wash., Friday Harbor, Wash.
Scripps Institution of Oceanography, Univ. of Calif., La Jolla, Calif.

SCIENTIFIC NAMES

Following are the scientific names of species illustrated in this book. Heavy type indicates pages where species appear; numbers in lighter type are caption numbers. The genus name is first, then the species. If the genus name is abbreviated, it is the same as the genus name mentioned just before it.

3 Mnemiopsis leidyi.
20 Lyngbya majuscula.
21 Codium fragile.
22 1. Cladophora gracilis; 2. Ulva lactuca; 3a. Enteromorpha intestinalis; 3b. E. compressa.
23 1. Caulerpa prolifera; 2. Bryopsis plumosa.
24 1. Halimeda tuna; 2. Acetabularia crenulata; 3. Penicillus dumetosus.
25 1a. Sargassum natans; 1b. S. vulgare.
26 1. Alaria esculenta; 2. Padina pavonia; 3. Chordaria flagelliformis.

(Scientific Names Continued)

27 1. Ectocarpus viridis; 2a. Desmarestia viridis; 2b. D. aculeata; 3. Chorda tomentosa.
28 1. Agarum cribrosum; 2a. Laminaria agardhii; 2b. L. digitata.
29 1. Macrocystis pyrifera; 2. Postelsia palmaeformis; 3. Nereocystis luetkeana.
30 1a. Fucus vesiculosus; 1b. F. evanescens.
31 Dasya sp.
32 1a. Gigartina stellata; 1b. G. corymbifera; 1c. G. microphylla; 2. Chondrus crispus (3 forms); 3a. Gelidium coulteri; 3b. G. corneum.
33 1a. Polysiphonia fibrillosa; 1b. P. nigrescens; 1c. P. harveyi; 2. Grinnellia americana; 3a. Spermothamnion turneri; 3b. S. baileyi.
34 1a. Ceramium fastigiatum; 1b. C. rubrum; 2a. Plumaria serecea; 2b. P. pectinata; 3a. Porphyra umbilicalis; 3b. P. atropurpurea.
35 Corallina officinalis.
40 1. Ciona intestinalis; 2. Molgula manhattensis.
41 1. Leucosolenia botryoides; 2. Scypha lingua.
42 1. Microciona prolifera; 2. Cliona celata.
43 1. Callyspongia vaginalis; 2. Haliclona occulata; 3. Hippiospongia lachne; 4. H. canaliculata; 5. H. equinoformis.
45 1. Aurelia aurita; 2. Cyanea capillata.
46 1. Gonionemus murbachii; 2. Tubularia spectabilis; 3. Obelia gelatinosa.
47 Physalia physalis.
48 1. Metridium dianthus; 2. Adamsia sociabilis; 3a. Sagartia modesta; 3b. S. luciae.
49 Cribrina xanthogrammica.
50 1. Balanophylla elegans; 2. Astrangia danae; 3. Oculina diffusa.
51 1. Corallium rubrum; 2. Agaricia agaricites; 3. Acropora cervicornis; 4. Favia fragum; 5. Diploria labyrithiformis.
52 1. Pennatula aculeata; 2. Gorgonia flabellum; 3. Plexaura flexuosa.
53 1. Folia parallela; 2. Pleurobrachia brunnea.
54 Cerebratulus lacteus.
55 Nereis virens.
56 Bispira sp.
57 1. Aphrodite aculeata; 2. Pectinaria gouldii; 3. Cirratulus grandis; 4. Chaetopterus pergamentaceus; 5. Arenicola cristata.
58 1. Membranipora pilosa; 2. Bugula turrita; 3. Crisea eburnea.
59 1. Terebratulina spitzbergensis; 2. T. septentrionalis; 3. Lingula anatina.
61 1. Amphipholis squamata; 2. Gorgonocephalus arcticus; 3. Ophioderma brevispinum; 4. Ophiopholis aculeata; 5. Ophiothrix angulata.
62 1. Henricia sanguinolenta; 2. Ctenodiscus crispatus; 3. Asterias vulgaris; 4. Solaster endeca; 5. Echinaster sentus; 6. Asterias forbesi.
63 1. Patiria miniata; 2. Linckia columbiae; 3. Henricia leviuscula; 4. Pycnopodia helianthoides; 5. Pisaster ochraceus.
64 1. Cidaris tribuloides; 2. Arbacia punctulata; 3. Echinarachnius parma.
65 1. Arbacia punctulata; 2. Strongylocentrotus droebachiensis; 3. S. franciscanus; 4. Echinometra lucunter; 5. Encope emarginata; 6. Dendraster excentricus; 7. Echinarachinus parma.
66 1. Stichopus californicus; 2. Leptosynapta inhaerens; 3. Caudina arenata; 4. Cucumaria frondosa.
68 1. Lepas fascicularis; 2. Balanus balanoides.
69 1. Gammarus locusta; 2. Talorchestia longicornis; 3. Orchestoidea californiana; 4. Orchestia agilis.
70 1. Squilla empusa; 2. Penaeus setiferus; 3. Crangon septemspinosa.
71 1. Homarus americanus; 2. Panulirus argus.
72 1. Emerita analoga; 2. E. talpoida.

(Scientific Names Continued)

73 Pagurus pollicaris.
74 1. Callinectes sapidus; 2. Carcinides maenas.
75 1. Portunus gibbesii; 2. Ovalipes ocellatus.
76 1. Cancer irroratus; 2. C. borealis; 3. C. magister.
77 1. Uca pugnax; 2. Ocypode quadrata.
78 1. Pugettia producta; 2. Libinia emarginata; 3. L. dubia.
79 1. Eurypterus fischeri; 2. Limulus polyphemus.
81 1. Chaetopleura apiculata; 2. Mopalia ciliata; 3. Ischnochiton magdalensis.
83 1. Nucula proxima; 2. Acila castrensis; 3. Nuculana minuta; 4. N. taphria; 5. N. acuta.
84 1. Arca umbonata; 2. Anadara ovalis; 3. Arca zebra; 4. Anadara notabilis; 5. Barbatia bailyi.
85 1. Mytilus edulis; 2. Volsella demissa; 3. V. modiolus; 4. Brachidontes recurvus.
86 1. Aequipecten gibbus; 2. Chlamys ornatus; 3. Hinnites multirugosus.
87 1. Chlamys hericius; 2. Leptopecten latiaruatus; 3. Chlamys sentis; 4. Placopecten magellanicus; 5. Pecten diegensis; 6. Aequipecten irradians.
88 1. Anomia simplex; 2. A. aculeata; 3. A. peruviana.
89 1. Ostrea lurida; 2. Plicatula gibbosa; 3. Crassostrea virginica.
90 1. Atrina serrata; 2. A. rigida; 3. Pinna carnea.
91 1. Pteria colymbus; 2. P. nebulosa.
92 1. Pandora gouldiana; 2. P. trilineata; 3. P. punctata; 4. P. filosa.
93 1. Astarte undata; 2. A. castanea; 3. A. striata; 4. A. alaskensis; 5. A. esquimalti.
94 1. Lucina floridana; 2. Phacoides annulatus; 3. Codakia orbicularis; 4. Lucina pensylvanica.
95 1. Clinocardium ciliatum; 2. Trachycardium muricatum; 3. Clinocardium nutalli; 4. Dinocardium robustum.
96 1. Mercenaria campechiensis; 2. M. mercenaria.
98 1. Protothaca tenerrima; 2. P. staminea; 3. P. lacineata.
99 1. Macrocallista maculata; 2. M. nimbosa.
100 1. Dosinia elegans; 2. D. discus; 3. Gemma gemma.
101 Tivela stultorum.
102 1. Tellina bodegensis; 2. T. carpenteri; 3. T. radiata; 4. T. salmonea; 5. T. modesta; 6. T. interrupta; 7. T. lineata.
103 1. Macoma tenta; 2. M. balthica; 3. M. constricta; 4. M. secta; 5. M. indentata; 6. M. nasuta.
104 1. Donax denticulata; 2. D. fossor; 3. D. californicus; 4. D. gouldi; 5. D. variablis.
105 1. Solen rosaceus; 2. Ensis directus; 3. Solen viridis; 4. Tagelus plebeius.
106 1. Mactra fragilis; 2. Spisula solidissima.
107 1. Mulinia lateralis; 2. Laviosa lineata; 3. L. plicatella.
108 1. Mya truncata; 2. M. arenaria.
109 1. Cyrtopleura costata; 2. Petricola pholadiformis; 3. Barnea truncata.
110 Teredo navalis.
112 1. Megathura crenulata; 2. Acmaea scabra; 3. A. antillarum; 4. Diodora listeri; 5. Acmaea testudinalis.
113 1. Turbo castaneus; 2. Calliostoma ligatum; 3. Margarites groenlandicus; 4. Calliostoma tampaense; 5. C. doliarium.
114 1. Tegula funebralis; 2. T. gallina; 3. T. fasciata.
115 1. Haliotis rufescens; 2. H. kamtschatkana; 3. H. fulgens; 4. H. cracherodi.
116 1. Epitonium rupicolum; 2. E. greenlandicum; 3. Opalia wroblewskii; 4. Epitonium multistriatum.
117 1. Natica clausa 2. N. canrena; 3. Polinices duplicatus; 4. Lunatia heros.
118 1. Crepidula onyx; 2. C. aculeata; 3. C. nummaria; 4. C. forni-

(Scientific Names Continued)

cata; 5. C. convexa; 6. C. plana.

119 1. Littorina scutulata; 2. L. planaxis; 3. L. saxatilis; 4. L. irrorata; 5. L. littorea; 6. L. angulifera.

120 1. Strombus raninus; 2. Cassis tuberosa; 3. Strombus alatus.

121 1. Strombus pugilis; 2. S. gigas; 3. Cassis madagascariensis; 4. C. flammea.

122 1. Bittium alternatum; 2. Cerithidea californica; 3. Batillaria minima; 4. Cerithium floridanum.

123 1. Tonna galea; 2. T. maculosa; 3. Ficus communis.

125 1. Zonaria spadicea; 2. Cypraea spurca; 3. C. cinerea; 4. C. zebra; 5. Pusula solandri; 6. P. californiana; 7. Trivia quadripunctata; 8. T. pediculus.

126 1. Murex pomum; 2. M. florifer; 3. Eupleura caudata; 4. Murex gemma.

127 1. Murex festivus; 2. M. trialatus; 3. M. cabriti; 4. Ocenebra interfossa; 5. O. circumtexta.

128 1. Purpura patula; 2. Urosalpinx cinerea; 3. Thais lima; 4. T. emarginata; 5. T. lapillus.

129 1. Mitrella carinata; 2. M. lunata; 3. Columbella mercatoria; 4. Anachis avara.

130 1. Busycon canaliculatum; 2. B. carica; 3. Neptunea tabulata; 4. N. decemcostata.

131 1. Busycon contrarium; 2. B. spiratum; 3. Buccinum undatum; 4. B. glaciale.

132 1. Nassarius obsoletus; 2. N. vibex; 3. N. trivittatus; 4. N. fossatus.

133 1. Fasciolaria hunteria; 2. Pleuroploca gigantea; 3. Fasciolaria tulipa.

134 1. Oliva sayana; 2. Olivella mutica; 3. O. baetica; 4. O. biplicata.

135 1. Conus californicus; 2. C. mus; 3. C. regius; 4. C. floridanus; 5. C. spurius.

136 1. Bulla gouldiana; 2. Haminoea solitaria; 3. Hydatina vesicaria; 4. Bulla occidentalis; 5. B. striata.

137 1. Dendronotus frondosus; 2. Aeolis papillosa.

138 Octopus vulgaris.

139 1. Illex illecebrosus; 2. Ommas trephes illexillecebrosus; 3. Octopus bimaculatus.

140 1. Dentalium entale stimsoni; 2. D. laqueatum; 3. D. entale; 4. D. eboreum; 5. D. pretiosum.

141 Prunus maritimus.

142 1. Uniola paniculata; 2. Ipomoea pes-caprae; 3. Zostera marina.

143 1. Ilex vomitoria; 2. Cenchrus tribuloides; 3. Salicornia europaea; 4. Scirpus americanus; 5. Solidago sempervirens.

144 1. Lupinus arboreus; 2. Mesembryanthemum aequilaterale; 3. Lathyrus maritimus; 4. Fragaria chiloensis; 5. Convolvulus soldanella.

145 1. Phragmites communis; 2. Erigeron glaucus; 3a. Abronia umbellata; 3b. A. latifolia.

146 1. Serenoa repens; 2. Sabal palmetto; 3. Myrica cerifera; 4. Caccolobis uvifera; 5. Rhizophora mangle.

147 Pelacanus occidentalis.

148 1. Haemotopus palliatus; 2. Charadrius hiaticula semipalmatus; 3. Arenaria interpres morinella; 4. Limnodromus griseus; 5. Catoptrophorus semipalmatus.

149 1. Recurvirostra americana; 2. Calidris canutus rufus; 3. Crocethia alba; 4. Erolia melanotos; 5. Ereunetes mauri.

150 1. Larus argentatus; 2. L. articilla; 3. L. delawarensis; 4. L. occidentalis; 5. L. californicus.

151 1. Thalasseus maximus; 2. Sterna hirundo; 3. S. paradisaea; 4. S. forsteri; 5. Rynchops nigra; 6. Larus marinus.

152 1. Mycteria americana; 2. Guara alba; 3. Phalacrocorax auritus; 4. Anhinga anhinga.

153 1. Ardea herodias; 2. Florida caerulea; 3. Dichromanassa rufescens; 4. Casmerodius albus egretta.

INDEX

Abalones, 115
Acetabularia, 24
Activities for amateurs, 6-7
Adamsia, 48-49
Agarum, 28
Alaria, 26, 28
Algae, 18-35; see *also specific names*
Alternate Bittium, 122
American Lobster, 71
Amethyst Gem Clam, 100
Anemones, Sea, 48-49
Angel Wings, 109
Anhinga, 152
Animal life in sea, 36-40
Arctic Tern, 151
Ark Shells, 84
Arthropods, 67-79
family tree, 67
Ascidians, 40
Astartes, 93
Astrangia, 50-51
Avocets, 149

Balanophylla, 50-51
Band Shells, 133
Barnacles, 68
Basket Shells, 132
Basket Stars, 61
Bath Sponges, 43
Bayberry, 146
Beaches, 10-11, 14-15
Beach Fleas, 69
Beach Morning-glory, 144-145
Beach Pea, 144
Beach Plum, 141
Birds, 147-153; see *also specific names*
Bittium, Alternate, 122
Bivalves, 82-110
parts of, 82; see *also specific names*
Black Skimmer, 150-151
Blue Crab, 74
Blue-green Algae, 20
Boat Shells, 118
Books, 141, 147, 154
Brachiopods, 59
Brain Coral, 51
Brittle Stars, 60, 61
Brown Algae, 25-30
Bryopsis, 21, 23
Bryozoans, 58
Bubble Shells, 136
Buccinum, Common Northern, 131
Butterfly Shell, 104

Cabbage Palmetto, 146
Calico Clam, 99
Calico Crab, 75
California Gull, 150
Callithamnion, 33
Cask Shells, 123
Caspian Tern, 151
Caulerpa, 23
Ceramium, 34
Cerebratulus, 54
Ceriths, 122
Chalina, 42-43
Checkerboard, 99
Cherrystone Clams, 96
Chestnut Clams, 93
Chestnut Turban, 113
Chitons, 81
Chondrus, 32
Chorda, 27
Chordaria, 26
Cidaris, 64
Ciona, 40
Cladophora, 22
Clams, 96-101, 105-108; see *also specific names*
Clam Worm, 55
Cliona, 42
Cockle Shells, 95
Codium, 21
Coelenterates, 44-52
see *also specific names*
Coffee Bean Shells, 124-125
Comb Jellies, 3, 53
Common Egret, 153
Common Tern, 151
Communities, seashore, 37
Conch Shells, 120-121
Florida Horse Conch, 133
Cone Shells, 135
Copepods, 16
Coquina Shells, 104
Corallina, 35
Corals, 40, 50-52
Cormorant, Double-crested, 152
Cowries, 124-125
Crabs, 73-79; see *also specific names*
Cribrina, 49
Crinoids, 60
Cucumbers, Sea, 66

Daisy, Seaside, 145
Dasya, 31
Deadman's Fingers, 42-43
Desmarestia, 27
Diatoms, 16
Dinoflagellates, 16-17
Dogwinkles, 128
Donax Shells, 104
Dosinias, 100
Dove-shells, 129
Dowitcher, 148
Drills, 126, 128
Duck Clams, 107
Dune plants, 141-146
Dwarf Tritons, 127

Echinoderms, 60-66
family tree, 60
Ectocarpus, 27
Edible Rock Crab, 76
Edible Shrimp, 70
Eelgrass, 142
Egrets, 153
Enteromorpha, 22
Eurypterid, 79
Eyed Coral, 50

Fan Worm, 56
Featherweed, 34
Fiddler Crabs, 77
Fig Shell, 123
Fleas, Beach, 69

Florida Horse Conch, 133
Foraminifera, 16
Forster's Tern, 151
Fringed Worm, 56-57
Fucus, 30

Gammarus, 69
Gastropods, 111-137
parts of, 111; see *also specific names*
Gelidium, 32
Gem Clam, Amethyst, 100
Ghost Crabs, 77
Gigartina, 32
Glasswort, 143
Glory-of-the-Seas, 135
Glove Sponge, 43
Goldenrod, 143
Gonionemus, 46
Gooseneck Barnacles, 68
Grantia, 41
Graptolites, 9
Grass Sponge, 43
Great Black-backed Gull, 150-151
Great Blue Heron, 153
Green Algae, 21-24
Green Crab, 74-75
Green Heron, 153
Grinnellia, 33
Gulls, 150-151

Hairy Mopalia, 81
Halimeda, 24
Hard-shell Clams, 96-97
Heart Shells, 95
Helix Margarite, 113
Helmet Shells, 120-121
Hermit Crab, 49, 73
Herons, 153
Herring Gull, 150
Hornshells, 122
Horny Corals, 52
Horny Sponges, 42-43
Horseshoe Crab, 79
Hydroids, 40

Ibis, 152
Irish Moss, 32

Jackknife Clams, 105
Jellyfish, 44-47; see *also specific names*
Jingle Shells, 88
Jonah Rock Crab, 76

Kelp Crab, 78
Kelps, 28-29, 36
Key to seashore life, 4-5
King Crab, 79
Kitten's Paw, 89
Knots, 149

Ladder Shells, 116
Lady Crab, 75
Laminaria, 28
Lamp Shells, 59
Laughing Gull, 150
Laver, 34
Leaf Coral, 51
Leucosolenia, 41
Lime Sponges, 41
Limpets, 112
Linckia, 63
Lingula, 59
Little Blue Herons, 153
Littleneck Clams (Atlantic), 96
Littleneck Clams (Pacific), 98
Lobsters, 71
Long Clams, 108
Lucinas, 94
Lugworm, 56-57
Lupines, 144
Lyonsias, 92

Macoma Shells, 103
Macrocystis, 28-29
Mactras, 106-107
Mangrove, 146
Man-of-War, Portuguese, 47
Mantis Shrimp, 70
Mermaid's Cup, 24
Mermaid's Hair, 20
Merman's Shaving Brush, 24
Metridium, 48
Microciona, 42
Mole Crabs, 72
Mollusks, 80-140
family tree, 80; see *also specific names*
Moon Jellyfish, 45
Moon Shells, 117
Morning-glory, Beach, 144-145
Moss
Irish, 32
Sea, 23
Moss Animals, 58
Mud flat, 37
Murex Shells, 126-127
Museums, 154
Mussels, 85
Myrtle, Wax, 146

Nassas, 132
Naticas, 117
Neptune, Tabled, 130
Nereocystis, 28-29
Nut Clams, 83

Obelia, 44, 46
Octopus, 138-139
Oculina, 50-51
Olive Shells, 134
Oystercatchers, 148
Oyster Drills, 128
Oysters, 89
Pearl, 91

Padina, 26
Palmettos, 146
Pandora Shells, 92
Parchment Worm, 56-57
Pea, Beach, 144
Peacock Tail, 26
Pearl Oysters, 91
Pectens, 86-87
Pectoral Sandpiper, 149
Pelecypods, 82
Pelican, Brown, 147
Penicillus, 24
Pennatula, 52
Pen Shells, 90
Periwinkles, 119
Pink Jellyfish, 45
Pismo Clam, 101
Plankton, 16-17
Plants, 141-146
in the sea, 36; see *also specific names*
Pleurobrachia, 53
Plover, Semipalmated, 148
Plumaria, 34
Polyp animals, 44

Polysiphonia, 33
Pompano Shell, 104
Porphyra, 34
Portuguese Man-of-war, 47
Portunus Crab, 75
Precious Coral, 51
Prehistoric sea life, 9
Protozoa, 40
Ptilota, 34
Purpuras, 128

Quahogs, 96-97

Radiolarians, 17
Railroad Vine, 142
Rainbow Jelly, 3
Razor Clams, 105
Red Algae, 31-35
Reddish Egret, 153
Reed, 145
Ribbon Worms, 54
Ring-billed Gull, 150
Rock Barnacles, 68
Rock Crabs, 76
Rock Venus Shells, 98
Rockweed, 30
Royal Tern, 151
Ruddy Turnstone, 148
Rush, Shore, 143

Sagartia, 48-49
Sandbugs, 72
Sandbur, 143
Sand Crabs, 77
Sand Dollars, 64-65
Sanderling, 149
Sand Hoppers, 69
Sandpipers, 149
Sand Shrimp, 70
Sand Strawberry, 144
Sand Verbena, 145
Sandworms, 55
Sargassum, 25
Saw Palmetto, 146
Scallops, 86-87
Scientific names, 154-157
Sea Anemones, 48-49
Sea Bat, 63
Sea Biscuits, 64
Sea Cucumbers, 60, 66
Sea Fan, 52
Sea-fig, 144
Sea-grape (tree), 146
Sea Grapes (animals), 40
Sea Lettuce, 22
Sea Moss, 23
Sea Mouse, 56-57
Sea-oats, 142
Sea Palm, 28-29
Sea Pen (coelenterate), 52
Sea Pens (bivalve), 90
Sea Plume, 52
Seas, contents of, 8-9
Seashores, 10-11, 14-15
Seaside Daisy, 145
Seaside Goldenrod, 143
Sea Slugs, 136, 137
Sea Snails, 111
Sea Squirts, 40
Sea Stars, 62-63
Sea Urchins, 60, 64-65
Seaweeds, 18-35
Sea Whip, 52
Segmented worms, 55-57
Semipalmated Sandpiper, 149
Shark Eye, 117
Sheep's Wool Sponge, 43
Shipworms, 110
Shorelines, 3, 8, 10-11
Shore Rush, 143
Shrimp, 70
Slipper Shells, 118
Slugs, Sea, 137
Snails, Mud, 132
Snowy Egret, 153
Soft-shell Clams, 108
Spermothamnion, 33
Spider Crabs, 78
Spiny Lobster, 71
Sponges, 41-43; *see also specific names*
Sponge Seaweed, 21
Squid, 138-139
Staghorn Coral, 51
Staircase Shells, 116
Star Coral, 51
Starfish, 40, 61-63
Steamer Clams, 108
Stony Corals, 50-51
Stout Tagelus, 105
Suberites, 42
Sunray Venus, 99
Surf Clams, 106-107
Swimming Crabs, 74-75

Tabled Neptune, 130
Talorchestia, 69
Tegula Shells, 114
Tellin Shells, 102
Teredo, 110
Terns, 151
Thracias, 92
Three-square, 143
Tide pool, 37
Tides, 12
Tooth Shells, 140
Top Shells, 113
Trees, 146
Tritons, Dwarf, 127
Trumpet Worm, 56-57
Tubularia, 46
Tulip Shells, 133
Tun Shells, 123
Turban Shells, 114
Turkey Wing, 84
Tusk Shells, 140

Univalves, 111-137 *see also specific names*

Vase Sponge, 43
Venus Girdle, 53
Verbena, Sand, 145

Wampum, 97
Water Turkey, 152
Waves, 13
Wax Myrtle, 146
Wedge Shells, 104
Wentletraps, 116
Western Gull, 150
Whale, Blue, 36
Whelks, 130-131
White Heron, 153
White Ibis, 152
White Shells, 94
Willet, 148
Wind and waves, 13
Wing Oysters, 91
Wood Stork, 152
Worms, 40, 54-57; *see also specific names*

Yaupon, 142-143

MEASURING SCALE (IN TOTHS OF AN INCH)